Rhagair

Ar ôl i mi weld y lluniau yn y llyfr hwn, gallaf ddeall yn iawn
y rheswm dros eu cynnwys. Pam felly, meddech chi? Wel, oherwydd
fy mod i'n dioddef o Ddementia Fasgwlaidd, ac nid yw'n hawdd dod
o hyd i'r geiriau i esbonio pam na allwn gyfathrebu â chi. Rwy'n
credu'n gryf y bydd y llyfr hwn yn helpu i esbonio i bobl beth
yw dementia, a sut mae'n effeithio arnon ni.

Yn ôl yr hen ddywediad, mae un llun yn werth mil o eiriau - ac
mae hyn yn sicr yn wir yn ein hachos ni. Felly, mae angen i chi
edrych ar y lluniau a gweld beth maen nhw'n ceisio'i ddweud
wrthych chi. Y dudalen sy'n sefyll allan i mi yw'r un sy'n
dweud 'Pobl 1; Tuniau o ffa pob 0' oherwydd ei bod yn pwysleisio
ymroddiad y bobl sy'n gofalu amdanon ni. Cymerwch eich amser
i edrych drwy'r llyfr i ddod o hyd i'r rhan sydd ag arwyddocâd
arbennig i chi.

Yna, ewch ati i fyw eich bywyd yn llawn.
Antur cyn Dementia.

Dr Trevor Jarvis EDE BEM

Gair gan yr Awdur...

Ers tro byd bellach, dementia yw'r 'eliffant yn yr ystafell' - yn rhy fawr i'w anwybyddu, ac eto rydyn ni'n dal i hwfro o'i gwmpas . . .

Yn y dafarn, byddai pobl yn dweud jôcs am glefyd Alzheimer, a finnau'n meddwl, 'Fydden nhw byth yn dweud y fath beth petai rhywun yn dioddef o ganser.' Sylweddolais bryd hynny, petaen nhw'n gwybod mwy am y peth, y bydden nhw'n ailfeddwl.

Collais fy mam-gu i ddementia, ac oherwydd y gofal diflino a roddodd iddi bu farw fy mam innau'n annhymig. Cafodd fy mam-yng-nghyfraith ddiagnosis o ddementia yn 59 oed, a bellach mae ein bywydau ni fel teulu'n troi o'i chwmpas hi er mwyn ei chefnogi hyd eithaf ein gallu. Mae dementia'n debyg i rywun sydd wedi glanio'n ddiwahoddiad i mewn i'ch teulu a'ch cartref. Nid yw'n gwahaniaethu, ac mae'n aml yn gwbl ddidostur - ond, ymhlith yr holl ddagrau a'r adlais o 'Pam fi?', mae pyliau o chwerthin i'w clywed o hyd. Mae bod dan warchae yn aml yn arwain at berthynas agosach, at ddathlu'r pethau bach mewn bywyd, ac at gysylltiad agos rhwng aelodau o'r teulu.

Dros y blynyddoedd diwethaf, rwyf wedi gweithio gydag ysbiwyr, pêl-droedwyr, dawnswyr a pheilotiaid rhyfel - pob un ohonynt bellach yn dioddef o ddementia. Rwy'n ymweld â nifer o gartrefi gofal i

weithio gyda'r staff, ac wedi sylweddoli bod gweld dim ond y dementia mewn person yn debyg i edrych ar eu cysgod, heb siarad gyda nhw. Mae'n bwysig cofio pa un ddaeth gyntaf - y person, nid y dementia.

Roeddwn yn awyddus i gael llyfr sy'n crisialu'r rhwystredigaeth a'r heriau a wynebir gan unigolion, teuluoedd a staff gofal. Llyfr y gallai plant ei ddarllen a'i ddeall. Llyfr oedd yn dangos y gall dementia effeithio ar bob un ohonom, a pha mor bwysig yw dangos empathi.

Gobeithiaf y bydd y llyfr hwn yn ysgogi'r chwerthin a'r dagrau, fel ei gilydd. Mae'r iaith yn syml ac yn rhydd o jargon. Trwy'r defnydd cynnil o luniau a geiriau, gobeithio bod yma le hefyd i'ch teimladau a'ch emosiynau chithau i'ch helpu i ddod i well dealltwriaeth o ddementia ac i ddangos i eraill gymaint yw eich consýrn amdanynt.

Does neb yn gorfod bod ar ei ben ei hun. Peidiwch byth â bod yn rhy ofnus nac yn rhy falch i ofyn am help.

Gyda'n gilydd, rydyn ni'n gryfach.

Diolch...

Gyda'r llyfr bach hwn, rydw i wedi gwireddu uchelgais nad o'n i hyd yn oed yn sylweddoli ei bod gen i.

Diolch o galon i Em am fod yn wraig a mam gwbl arbennig, ac yn ferch amhrisiadwy.

Diolch i Liz, Annie, Billy, Dad, Anna, Lulu y milgi a Johnny am eich cefnogaeth barhaus.

Rhaid i mi ddiolch i Richard Hawkins a phawb yng nghwmni cyhoeddi Hawker am eu ffydd yn fy syniad o'r cychwyn cyntaf. Ac yn olaf, diolch i Chris Mitchell am droi yr athro hwn yn ddisgybl i bob person rwy'n cwrdd â nhw ym maes gofal dementia.

Rwy'n sylweddoli bod pawb y dyddiau hyn yn brin o un

peth - sef amser - felly mae'r llyfr hwn yn fyr, yn syml ac yn uniongyrchol heb wastraffu geiriau. Mae gan lawer o lyfrau am ddementia un peth yn gyffredin rhyngddynt - unwaith rydych yn eu rhoi o'ch llaw, wnewch chi byth eu codi eto.

Hoffwn feddwl y bydd y llyfr bach hwn yn wahanol, ac yn rhoi cyfle i chi gael y sgyrsiau rydych wedi bod yn eu gohirio ers tro.

Gadewch i'ch meddyliau chi ysgrifennu'r gweddill.

O enau plant bychain...

Safodd fy merch 10 oed ar lwyfan y Theatre Royal yng Nghaerefrog mewn 'Noson i'w Chofio' - sef cyngerdd er budd Cymdeithas Alzheimer - a sôn wrth yr 850 o oedolion yn y gynulleidfa am 'Mam-gu'. Alla i ddim mynegi mewn geiriau pa mor falch o'n i ohoni.

'Weithiau, dyw oedolion ddim yn deall y pethau pwysig.'

'Cyn i Mam-gu gael ei heffeithio, doedd gen i ddim syniad beth oedd dementia. Do'n i erioed wedi clywed am glefyd Alzheimer.'

'Mae llawer yn meddwl mai dim ond pobl llawer hŷn sy'n cael dementia. Doedd Mam-gu'n ddim ond 58 oed.'

'Y diwrnod y cafodd Mam-gu ei diagnosis o ddementia oedd y diwrnod y cafodd PAWB ohonon ni eu heffeithio.'

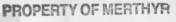

'Nid dim ond unigolion sy'n cael dementia - mae'r teulu cyfan yn ei gael. Mae'n bwysig ein bod ni i gyd yn gweithio gyda'n gilydd FEL TÎM.'

'Mae Mam-gu'n dal i edrych yr un fath.'

'Rydyn ni'n dal i ganu yn y stryd, mynd â'r ci am dro, chwerthin gyda'n gilydd, bwydo'r adar, a dawnsio i gerddoriaeth ar y radio. Weithiau dwi'n aros y nos gyda hi - mae hi'n gadael i mi aros lan yn hwyr a gwylio rhaglenni teledu nad ydw i'n cael eu gweld fel arfer.'

'Os ydyn ni am helpu rhywun, rhaid i ni WYBOD beth yn union yw'r broblem.'

'Unwaith y cafodd Mam-gu y diagnosis, roedden ni'n gwybod â beth roedden ni'n delio.'

'Ond dyw bywyd ddim yn dod i stop gyda chlefyd Alzheimer.'

'Ers cael y diagnosis, mae Mam-gu wedi dawnsio ar y llwyfan mewn sioe gerdd, ac wedi cwrdd â chanwr enwog. Mae'r teulu hefyd wedi bod yn Efrog Newydd.'

'Mae Mam-gu'n dal yn seren.
Mae Mam-gu'n dal yn llawn hwyl.
Mae Mam-gu'n dal i allu sglefrio am yn ôl.
Mam-gu yw hi o hyd.
Ond mae Mam-gu'n anghofio…'

Felly DWI'N COFIO.

Annwyl Dementia,
Chest ti ddim gwahoddiad i ymuno â'n teulu ni,
ond rwyt ti yma nawr.
Gallen ni ganolbwyntio'n llwyr arnat ti,
ond yn lle hynny fe ganolbwyntiwn ar Mam-gu.

Annwyl Dementia,
Dwi wedi dy gael di
Dwyt ti ddim wedi fy nghael i!

Annwyl Dementia,
'Byddai dy dad yn 134 oed, Mair,'
meddai hi.
Fe ddyweda i wrtho pan ddaw i'm
nôl o'r ysgol.
Bydd e'n siŵr o'i rhoi hi yn ei lle!

Annwyl Dementia,
Cariodd Mam fi am 9 mis, fy mwydo,
fy nghadw'n saff.
Dysgu i mi'r gwahaniaeth rhwng
da a drwg.
Byddai wedi gwneud unrhyw beth
drosof i, bob dydd o'i bywyd.
Nid TI yn erbyn MAM yw hyn,
ond TI yn ein herbyn NI!

Annwyl Dementia,
Hoffwn i bawb WRANDO
arna i, yn hytrach
na dweud beth sydd
orau i mi!

Annwyl Dementia,

Dwi newydd lowcio
6 o Walnut Whips.

Nid arnat ti mae'r
bai - y fi sydd
wrth fy modd gyda
Walnut Whips!

Annwyl Dementia,
Mae fy merch wedi
blino'n lân.
Ai fi sy'n
gyfrifol am hyn?
Ynteu arnat ti
mae'r bai?
Mae croeso i ti
ddod ar fy ôl i,
ond plis gad
lonydd iddi hi.

Annwyl Dementia,
Mae fy ngŵr wedi mynd.
Does gen i ddim plant.
Dim ond TI a FI sydd ar ôl.
Gyda'n gilydd.

Ar ein pennau'n hunain...

Cyhoeddiadau personol

I osod cyhoeddiad, ffoniwch 01904 676767

Cwsg
mewn
Hedd

Annwyl Dementia,

Mae pawb yn gorffen fy mrawddegau drosof i.

Bob nos, mae gen i bentwr o atalnodau llawn ar ôl heb eu defnyddio.

Annwyl Dementia,
Fe fues i'n
llysieuwraig ar
hyd fy mywyd -
nes i ti gyrraedd.
Nawr, dwi'n
mwynhau bwyta
bacwn!

Annwyl Dementia,
Mae Mam-gu'n anghofio,
felly dwi'n cofio drosti hi.

Annwyl Dementia,

Ambell ddiwrnod dwi'n teimlo fel rhoi'r ffidil yn y to. Ond wedyn, dwi'n meddwl - beth petai'r esgid ar y droed arall?

Sut byddai Mam yn gofalu amdana i?

Annwyl Dementia,
Gallai'r ferch yma ennill mwy yn
llenwi silffoedd yn yr archfarchnad.
Diolch byth, mae'n well ganddi ofalu
amdanon ni.

Pobl	1
Tuniau o ffa pob	0

Annwyl Dementia,

Rwyt ti wedi newid y cloc yn ddim
ond llun crwn ar y wal.

Dwi'n dal i gofio 'o'r gloch'
a 'hanner awr wedi'.

Plis gad y rheiny i mi …

Mae amser yn werth y byd.

Annwyl Dementia,
Ar ôl cymharu'r gweithgareddau mewn cartref
gofal ac mewn carchar, dwi am
ddwyn arian o'r banc...

Annwyl Dementia,
Diolch byth fod fy ngwraig yn dathlu'r hyn
sydd ar ôl ohonof i,
yn hytrach na meddwl am yr hyn rwyt ti
wedi'i gymryd oddi arnaf.

Annwyl Dementia,
Mae'r dabled, neu'r llechen, yma'n
storio fy lluniau a 'nghaneuon.
Gallaf ei defnyddio i sgwrsio gyda
fy mab yn Awstralia. Pam nad oes
unrhyw sgil-effeithiau?

Annwyl Dementia,
Pe bai rhyw deyrn
yn dinistrio
bywydau cymaint
o'n hanwyliaid
ag rwyt ti'n ei
wneud, byddai'r
byd yn gwneud
popeth posib
i'w rwystro.

Annwyl Dementia,
Nid cyflwr ydw i.
Nid salwch ydw i.
Nid clefyd ydw i.
Nid symptom ydw i.

Delyth ydw i.

Annwyl Dementia,
Er bod gen i bobl o
'nghwmpas drwy'r adeg,
dwi'n teimlo mor UNIG.

Annwyl Dementia,

Dwi'n casáu mynd i siopa erbyn hyn.

"£15.67, os gwelwch yn dda."

Dwi'n dal fy llaw allan a gobeithio'r gorau.

Cymerwch fy arian, a rhoi'r nwyddau a'r newid i mi.

Plis peidiwch â holi.

Annwyl Dementia,

Wnei di plis rwystro Dad rhag dal
trên i Blackpool?

Yn y Blaenau mae e'n byw.

O na, dim eto...

MEHEFIN 2012
30 Mawrth

Annwyl Dementia,
Dwi'n anghofio enwau.
Yn anghofio dyddiadau.
Yn anghofio llefydd.
Yn anghofio apwyntiadau.

...Paid â'm hanghofio i!

Annwyl Dementia,

Gawson ni ddiwrnod hyfryd fel teulu ar lan y môr.

Sgod a sglods, hufen iâ, gwlychu'n traed yn y dŵr.

Fyddai neb wedi dyfalu dy fod ti yno gyda ni!

Annwyl Dementia,

Amser = rhifau

Dyddiad = rhifau

Ffôn = rhifau

Arian = rhifau

Coginio = rhifau

Does gen i ddim rhifau

oherwydd dy fod TI gen i.

Annwyl Dementia,

Mae hi'n dewis fy nillad, fy ngolchi, fy ngwisgo, gwneud fy ngwely, glanhau fy stafell, a chau fy sgidiau.

Atgoffa fi... be dwi'n ei wneud?

Annwyl Dementia,

Aberthais bopeth er mwyn i'm merch gael yr yrfa roedd hi'n ei haeddu. Nawr mae hi'n gorfod aberthu ei gyrfa er fy mwyn i. Nid BENTHYCIAD oedd e i fod.

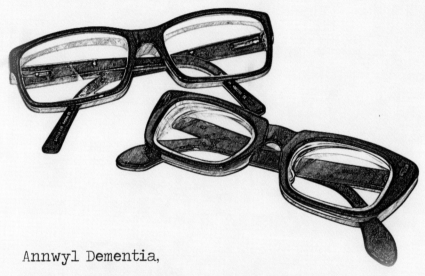

Annwyl Dementia,

Dwi wrth fy modd gyda'r boi Barker 'na
- beth yw ei enw e eto - o'r rhaglen
The Two Ronnies

Annwyl Dementia,

Es i weld y doctor heddiw.
Dywedodd fod gen i broblemau
gyda fy sgiliau gwybyddol,
fy llabed parwydol a'm llabed
gwegiliol. Mae'n rhaid nad wyt
ti gen i, neu fyddai hi byth
yn defnyddio geiriau mor
gymhleth! Fyddai hi?

Annwyl Dementia,

Dwi newydd glywed y gân honno ar y radio -
"Os arhoswch chithau'n hardd ac ifanc
Ni fydd cariad byth yn dianc."
Ro'n i wrth fy modd gyda hi erstalwm - ond nid erbyn
hyn.

Annwyl Dementia,

Fe rois i fath i Dad heddiw - a'm llygaid ar gau.
Er ei fwyn e.
Er fy mwyn i.
Er mwyn cadw'i urddas.
Dyweda wrtha i - pryd gawn ni agor ein llygaid?

Annwyl Dementia,

Uwd dydd Llun.
Uwd dydd Mawrth.
Uwd dydd Mercher.
Uwd bob blydi diwrnod.

Dwi'n difaru dweud 'mod
i'n hoffi uwd.

**Ydy uwd yn
foddion i dy
wella di?**

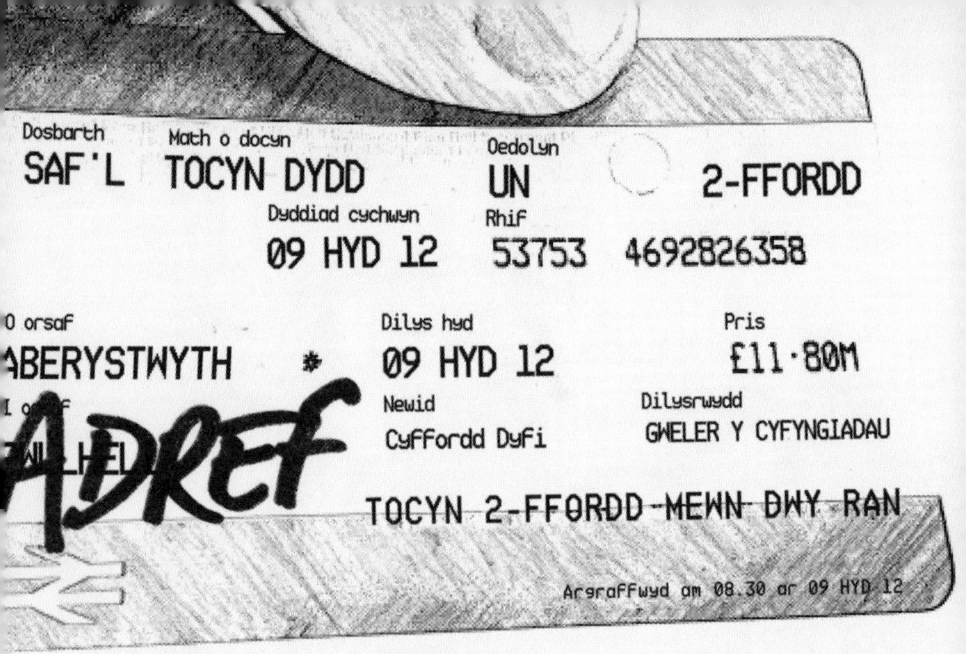

Annwyl Dementia,

"Ga i docyn un-ffordd, os gwelwch yn dda?"
"Wrth gwrs, syr - i ble hoffech chi fynd?"

"Adref."

Annwyl Dementia,

Nid ti yw fy mhroblem i.

Pobl eraill yw fy mhroblem i!

Annwyl Dementia,

"Ydy HI'n cymryd siwgr?"
"Ydy HI'n hoffi uwd?"
"Ydy HI eisiau mynd allan?"
Wyt ti wedi fy ngwneud i'n ANWELEDIG?

Ydw i wedi diflannu?

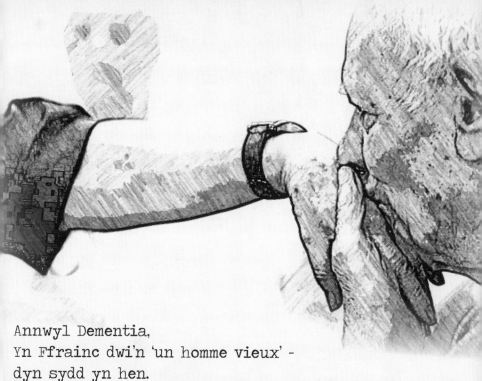

Annwyl Dementia,
Yn Ffrainc dwi'n 'un homme vieux' -
dyn sydd yn hen.
Yn Gymraeg dwi'n 'hen ddyn'.
Wnei di plis weld y DYN cyn gweld yr HEN?

Merci! Diolch!

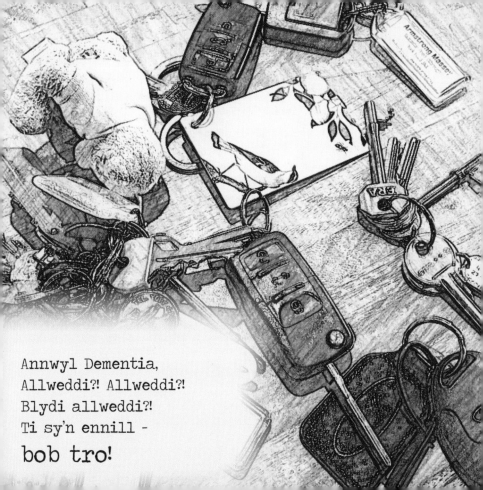

Annwyl Dementia,
Allweddi?! Allweddi?!
Blydi allweddi?!
Ti sy'n ennill -
bob tro!

Annwyl Dementia,

Maen nhw'n fy ngalw'n **"grwydryn"** am nad oes gen i ddim byd arall i'w wneud.

Fel arall, bydden nhw'n fy ngalw'n **"arddwr"** neu'n **"beintiwr"**

Annwyl Dementia,

Ro'n i'n arfer
mwynhau coginio,
ond mae coginio'n golygu
rhifau.
Sawl gram?
Sawl munud?
Sawl gradd?

...brechdan gaws fyddai
orau, dwi'n credu.

Annwyl Dementia,

Dwi'n falch eu bod nhw wastad yn cofio hyn:

nhw sy'n gweithio yn fy nghartref i,

nid fi sy'n byw yn eu gweithle nhw.

Annwyl Dementia,
Pan dwi'n chwilio am eiriau, mae llawer
ohonyn nhw wedi diflannu.
Mae'r un peth yn digwydd gydag enwau.
Ond mae cerddoriaeth yn aros.

Diolch am adael cerddoriaeth ar ôl i mi.

Annwyl Dementia,
Erstalwm, ro'n i'n crynu yn fy sgidiau pan oedd nodyn
ar fy ngwaith cartref -

"MAE ANGEN I TI 'NGWELD I".

Nawr, hoffwn ddweud y geiriau yna wrth sawl un.

Fe allen nhw "wneud yn well".

Annwyl Dementia,
Rhaid i mi ddechrau
cymryd fy nhabledi
newydd ddydd Iau.

Pryd mae
dydd Iau?

Annwyl Dementia,

"Dafydd, alli di gyfri i lawr o 100 i 0?"

"Alli di sillafu CARTREF am yn ôl?"

"Pa siâp sy'n wahanol?"

Pam na allan nhw wneud?

Erstalwm, roedd doctoriaid yn llawer mwy clyfar.

Annwyl Dementia,

Dwi'n gaeth ar ynys bellennig.

Mae 'na gwch yn cyrraedd.

Mae 'na bobl yn fy helpu am 10 munud,

ac yn sgrifennu pethau amdana i am 5 munud.

Wedyn maen nhw'n neidio'n ôl i mewn i'r cwch.

Brysiwch yma eto ...

Annwyl Dementia,

Pam mae Nain yn edrych ar f'ôl i,

mae hi'n hapus.

Ar yr un pryd, dwi'n edrych ar ôl
Nain, ac mae hynny'n fy ngwneud
innau'n hapus.

Rydyn ni'r
merched yn hoffi
cwmni'n gilydd.

Nain

Ela

Lulu!

Tydw
i'n
wych!

Annwyl Dementia,
Dydy'r ymwelwyr ddim yn defnyddio'n cwpanau ni.
Dydy'r gofalwyr ddim yn defnyddio'n cwpanau ni.
Atgoffa fi - beth sy'n bod arnon ni?

Wyt ti'n heintus?

Annwyl Dementia,
Petai rhywun yn gosod tudalen lân o bapur ar fy nrws,

beth allen nhw ei sgrifennu amdana i?

Annwyl Dementia,

Dwi'n mynd i gyngerdd Bryn Fôn heno.

Rhaid i ti aros adre rhag difetha'r hwyl.

Fe a' i â dillad isa glân a brwsh dannedd - jest rhag ofn.

Paid ag aros ar dy draed tan fydda i'n ôl!

☆ CYFLWYNO ☆   BRYN FÔN

BRYN FÔN
YN FYW

25 MEDI 2012

SEDD **25**   RHES **7**   DRWS **12**

SEDD **25**
RHES **7**
DRWS **12**

25 MEDI 2012
YN FYW

Annwyl Dementia,
Mae hyd yn oed siopau elusennol yn
gwrthod cymryd jig-sos os oes 'na
ddarnau ar goll.

Annwyl Dementia,

Mae fy nghartref gofal newydd wedi cael drws ffrynt fel f'un i.

Ro'n i'n meddwl ei fod yn syniad gwych.

Ond bob tro dwi'n ei agor mae'n addo cymaint ac yn rhoi dim byd ond

tor calon.

Annwyl Dementia,
Trawiad ar y galon? Wedi goroesi.
Canser? Wedi ei drechu.
Dementia? Yn dal wrthi.

Annwyl Dementia,
Mae merched dieithr yn fy nadwisgo,
rhoi cawod i mi a'm rhoi yn y gwely -
heb hyd yn oed gyflwyno'u hunain.
Doedd merched ddim mor bowld erstalwm.

Annwyl Dementia,
Diolch am beidio â dwyn fy ngallu i ddarllen eto. Ond
dwi wedi darllen pentwr o lyfrau amdanat ti - a does
dim diweddglo hapus i'r UN ohonyn nhw.

Annwyl Dementia,

Ro'n i'n arfer teimlo trueni dros anifeiliaid mewn sw.

Roedd pobl yn siarad amdanyn nhw drwy baen o wydr.

Does yr un anifail yn haeddu cael ei drin fel yna.

Annwyl Dementia,
Difaterwch? Na, byth.
Cydymdeimlad? Dim diolch.
Empathi? Ie, plis.

Annwyl Dementia,
Dwi'n edrych 'mlaen at fynd am bryd o fwyd gyda'r
teulu. Gobeithio y gallwn ni sgwrsio amdanyn NHW a FI.

NID amdanat ti!

Annwyl Dementia,
Dwi'n brwydro i anadlu ar ôl cael fy lapio
mewn gwlân cotwm.
Gad i mi roi cynnig arni.
Gad i mi fethu.
Gad i mi lwyddo.
Gad i mi fyw.

Annwyl Dementia,
Dwi wedi bod yn fyw am

74 mlynedd,
wedi magu 4 o blant a chael 11 o wyrion.

Ac eto,
does neb yn gwybod beth yw maint fy sgidiau i.

Annwyl Dementia,
Yr un galon sydd wedi curo y tu mewn i mi yn 5, 25, 45
a 95 oed.
Yr un galon. Yr un FI.

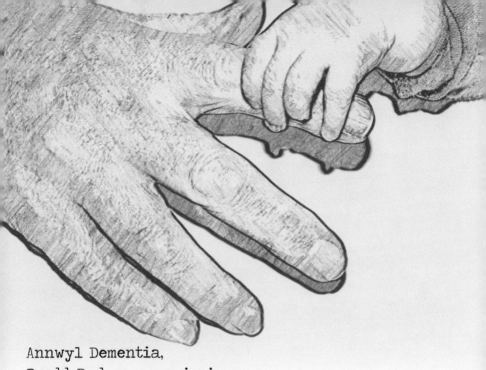

Annwyl Dementia,
Roedd Dad yn arwr i ni,
yn ein cadw'n saff bob amser.
Byddai wedi dringo'r goeden uchaf i'n hachub.
Trueni nad yw e'n gallu'n hachub o'th grafangau di.
Ond rwyt ti wedi concro'n harwr ni.

Annwyl Dementia,

Dydy fy hunangofiant ddim yn gyflawn.

Mae 'na sawl pennod ar ôl i'w sgrifennu.

Paid â'm hanfon i at yr argraffwyr eto...

Annwyl Dementia,
Yn yr ysbyty, claf ydw i.
Yn y cartref gofal, dwi'n ddefnyddiwr gwasanaeth.
Mewn gofal seibiant, gwestai ydw i.

Atgoffa fi - pwy ydw i?

Annwyl Dementia,
Dwi eisiau gwisgo fy welingtons,
nid fy sliperi.

Annwyl Dementia,

Mae'r twll yn y wal wedi llyncu fy ngherdyn banc.

Mae'n gwrthod ei roi'n ôl i mi.

Rhifau PIN?

Cyfrineiriau?

Cwestiynau cyfrinachol?

Trueni 'mod i wedi cael gwared â'r hen gadw-mi-gei.

Annwyl Dementia,

Diolch byth am Lwlw'r ci. Mae'n gwmni i mi, yn ffrind, ac yn mynd â fi allan am dro yn yr awyr iach. Mae'n f'atgoffa ei bod yn amser bwyd, ac mae pobl yn aros i siarad gyda ni. Hebddo fe, fyddai gen i ddim awydd gwneud dim - a byddet ti'n ennill.

Annwyl Dementia,
Sut gall pobl
barchu fy
nymuniadau heb
wybod beth ydyn
nhw?

Gofynnwch!

DEWCH I MEWN

Rydyn ni'n dal ar agor!

Annwyl Dementia,
Os nad yw dy hoff siop wedi cael stoc
newydd ers sbel, bydd llawer o'r 'stwff da'
wedi mynd. Dim ond mân bethau fydd ar ôl.
Paid â rhoi'r gorau i siopa yno. Mae arnyn
nhw angen dy gefnogaeth di.

Annwyl Dementia,
Pe baen ni'n dileu'r geiriau
"Pobl â Dementia"
ac yn rhoi "Plant" yn eu lle,
gan ddweud pa mor wael maen nhw'n
cael eu trin, byddai 'na helynt mawr.

Annwyl Dementia,

Dwi'n dal i allu darllen.

Mae'r geiriau'n dal yno.

Ond does dim ohonyn nhw'n gwneud synnwyr.

Fe fydda i'n arbed ffortiwn ar brynu llyfrau.

Annwyl Dementia,
Heddiw, galwodd Nesta
fi'n lleidr.
Fy nhŷ i - fy
nghardigan i.
Fy nhŷ i - fy mẁg i.
Fy nhŷ i - fy nannedd i.
Maen nhw'n fy siwtio i'n
well ta beth.

Annwyl Dementia,
Fe wnes i daro Annest heddiw.
Y tro cyntaf i mi wneud y
fath beth.
Fyddwn i byth yn ei tharo.
Ai fi darodd hi?
Ynteu ti wnaeth?
Neu'r ddau ohonon ni?

Annwyl Dementia,

Fe welais i'r dyn annwyl
'na eto heddiw.

Wn i ddim pwy yw e, ond
dwi'n gwybod 'mod i'n ei
garu.

Annwyl Dementia,

Mae dy gael di gyda mi'n debyg i chwarae

gêm fwrdd.

Ond rwyt ti wedi dwyn pob un o'r ysgolion, a gadael y nadroedd ar ôl.

Annwyl Dementia,
Daeth plant o'r ysgol leol aton ni heddiw. Roedden
ni wrth ein bodd. Doedden nhw ddim yn gallu dy
weld DI

- dim ond ein gweld NI.

Annwyl Dementia,
Dwi wedi cael llond bol ar wrando ar ryw ganeuon diflas, hen ffasiwn. Oes gen ti rywbeth gan y Tebot Piws?

Annwyl Dementia,
Diolch am ddangos i mi pwy
yw fy ffrindiau go iawn.

Annwyl Dementia,

Rydyn ni'n deulu mawr.

Hyd yma, dwyt ti ddim ond wedi cael gafael ar Dad.

Pam dwi'n gweld ôl fy nhraed yn y tywod tra bod pawb
arall yn claddu'u pennau ynddo, gan obeithio y byddi
di'n diflannu?

Annwyl Dementia,
Pa air alla i wneud?

Mae gen i U ac N ac I a G...

Annwyl Dementia,
Petai'r nyrsys ond yn gwybod
- Fy enw
- Rhif fy stafell
- Beth dwi'n hoffi ei fwyta a'i yfed
- Sut dwi'n edrych.

Mae ffermwr
yn gwybod
cymaint â
hynny am ei
wartheg!

Annwyl Dementia,

Rhaid bod fy wyres yn
wych mewn mathemateg.

Mae hi byth a beunydd
yn tap-tapio ar ei
chyfrifiannell.

Annwyl Dementia,

Er 'mod i'n 25 oed, mae pobl
yn siarad gyda fi fel
petawn i'n hen wraig.

Fe welais i'r fenyw yna eto
heddiw.

Tybed pwy yw hi?

Annwyl Dementia,
Os wyt ti wedi dod ar ôl Mam,
fe gei di drafferth.
Gyda'n gilydd, fe wnawn ein
gorau glas i'w chadw'n saff.

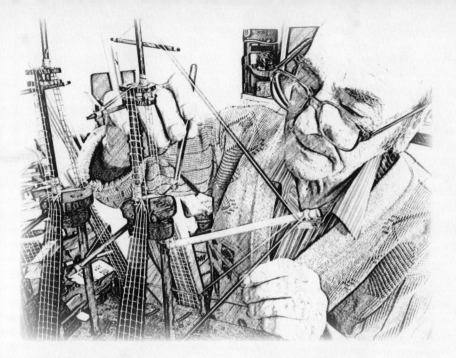

Annwyl Dementia,

Erstalwm, pan oedd rhywbeth yn torri, ro'n i'n gallu ei drwsio.

Trueni na alla i wneud yr un peth gyda ti heddiw.

Annwyl Dementia,

Rwyt ti wedi troi aelodau o 'nheulu i yn erbyn ei gilydd.

Trueni na allan nhw weld nad PWY sy'n iawn sy'n bwysig, ond BETH sy'n iawn.

Annwyl Dementia,
Gwniadwraig oedd Enid yn stafell 6 erstalwm, felly
maen nhw wedi rhoi gwaith gwnïo iddi hi.
Bownser o'n i - gobeithio nad ydyn nhw'n disgwyl i mi
ailafael yn fy ngwaith, yn 76 oed!

Annwyl Dementia,
Ti fydd yn ennill y
rhyfel yn y diwedd,
wrth gwrs.
Ond tan hynny mae
gennym lawer o
frwydrau i'w hennill!

Diolch i chi i gyd am eich help cwbl amhrisiadwy

Rwy'n siŵr o anghofio rhai pobl, felly maddeuwch i mi…

Pawb yn Alzheimer's Support, Wiltshire

Seiliwyd llawer o'r lluniau yn y llyfr hwn ar ffotograffau o waith Grant Newton a dynnwyd yng nghlwb dydd Alzheimer's Support, Devizes, Wiltshire

www.trainingforcarers.co.uk

Cherie Bakewell - fy nylunydd gwych

Alison, Kevin a phawb yn Peregrine House

Gill, Tony a phawb yn Riccall Carers

Jane, Wendy a phawb - Barnsley Dementia Champions

Lou Squires a phawb yn Millings a St John's House

Jill Shearer a phawb yn MMCG

Di a phawb yn The Hall

Mike Padgham a phawb yn yr ICG

Brian McGuire a'r tîm yn Visioncall

Gwasanaeth Ambiwlans Swydd Efrog

Pob un o'r Dementia Champions

Tommy a Joan Whitelaw

Bluebird Care

Chris Roberts a Jayne Goodrick

Gwên heintus Tony, a'r gerddoriaeth sy'n rhan ohono

Pam a Lucy a phawb yn Grimston Court

Caffi Dementia York Harmony

Hannah a Michael

Kim Pennock

Liz, Emma, Annie, Billy, Lulu

Graham Hodge

Andrew a Di a Thîm Wadell-Brown

Charlie Donaghy

Anna Oulton

Alison a Claire yn y Coach House

Leonnie Martin

Claire Tester

Pawb roddodd eu hamser yn rhad ac am ddim yn 'A Night to Remember'

Keith, Vince ac Agnes, Tow Law

Modryb Jennie, Beryl a Renee

Am eich cyfraniad artistig a chreadigol - Keara Stewart, Andy G a Steve Barnsley

Trevor Jarvis BEM EDE

Simone a phawb yn Woodlands

Kjartan Poskitt

Y dwymgalon Suzy Webster ac Alive Tim, sydd heb sylweddoli pa mor arbennig ydyn nhw

Ond yn fwy na dim i'r bobl anhygoel sy'n byw gyda dementia ac sy'n cyfoethogi fy mywyd bob dydd trwy siarad gyda mi.

Collins

Mandarin

Phrasebook
and Dictionary

Mandarin Phrasebook and Dictionary

Consultant: Joseph Zhou

Other languages in the
Collins Phrasebook and Dictionary series:
French, German, Greek, Italian, Japanese,
Polish, Portuguese, Spanish, Turkish.

HarperCollins Publishers
Westerhill Road, Bishopbriggs,
Glasgow G64 2QT

www.collinslanguage.com

First published 2008

Reprint 10 9 8 7 6 5 4 3 2 1 0

© HarperCollins Publishers 2008

ISBN 978-0-00-726461-2

Typeset by Davidson Pre-Press Graphics Ltd,
Glasgow

Printed in Malaysia by Imago

Essex County
Council Libraries

Contents

Introduction 4
Useful websites 5
Pronouncing Mandarin 6
Everyday photoguide 9
  Timetables 14
  Tickets 15
  Getting around 16
  Driving 20
  Shopping 23
  Keeping in touch 26
Key talk 27
Money 36
Getting around 39
  Airport 39
  Customs and passports 40
  Asking the way 41
  Bus and coach 44
  Metro 46
  Train 47
  Taxi 49
  Boat and ferry 51
Car 52
  Driving 52
  Petrol 53
  Problems/breakdown 54
  Car hire 55
Shopping 57
  Holiday 57
  Clothes 58
  Food 60
Daylife 63
  Sightseeing 63
  Leisure/interests 65
  Walking 66

Nightlife 68
  Popular 68
  Cultural 69
Accommodation 72
  Hotel (booking) 72
  Hotel (desk) 73
  Self-catering 74
Different travellers 76
  Children 76
  Special needs 77
  Exchange visitors 78
Difficulties 81
  Problems 81
  Complaints 82
  Emergencies 84
Health 86
Business 89
  Phoning 91
  Post office 94
  E-mail/fax 95
  Internet/cybercafé 96
Practical info 98
  Numbers 98
  Days and months 101
  Time 103
  Holidays and Festivals 106
Eating out 108
  Ordering drinks 110
  At the teahouse 111
  Ordering food 112
  Special requirements 114
  Eating photoguide 115
  Menu reader 124
Grammar 130
Dictionary 136

Your *Collins Mandarin Phrasebook and Dictionary* is a handy, quick-reference guide that will help make the most of your stay abroad. Its clear layout will save valuable time when you need that crucial word or phrase. Download free all the essential words and phrases you need to get by from www.collinslanguage.com/talk60. These hour long audio files are ideal for practising listening comprehension and pronunciation. The main sections in this book are:

Everyday China - photoguide
Packed full of photos, this section allows you to see all the practical visual information that will help with using cash machines, driving on motorways, reading signs, etc.

Phrases
Practical topics are arranged thematically with an opening section, Key talk, containing vital phrases that should stand you in good stead in most situations. Phrases are short, useful and each one has a pronunciation guide so that there is no problem saying them.

Eating out
This section contains phrases for ordering food and drink (and special requirements) plus a photoguide showing different places to eat, menus and practical information to help choose the best options. The menu reader allows you to work out what to choose.

Grammar
There is a short Grammar section explaining how the language works.

Dictionary
And finally, the practical English-Mandarin Dictionary means that you won't be stuck for words.

So, just flick through the pages to find the information you need and listen to the free audio download to improve your pronunciation.

Useful websites:

Accommodation
www.abouthotel.com
www.selfcateringchina.com
www.stayBeijing.com
www.venere.com

Currency Converter
www.x-rates.com

Driving
www.china-driving.com

Facts
www.cia.gov/library/publications
  /the-world-factbook

Foreign Office Advice
www.fco.gov.uk/travel
www.dfat.gov.au (Australia)
www.voyage.gc.ca (Canada)

Health advice
www.dh.gov.uk/travellers
www.thetraveldoctor.com
www.smartraveller.gov.au
  (Australia)
www.phac-aspc.gc.ca (Canada)

Information about China
www.china.org.cn
www.chinatoday.com
www.chinatour.com
www.cnto.org (China National
  Tourist Office)

Internet Cafés
www.cybercafes.com

Passport Office
www.ukpa.gov.uk
www.passports.gov.au (Australia)
www.pptc.gc.ca (Canada)

Sightseeing
www.china.com

Transport
www.travelchinaguide.com/
  china-trains
www.air-china.co.uk

Weather
www.bbc.co.uk/weather

It is not easy for foreigners to pronounce Mandarin so in this phrasebook we have used standard Latin phonetic sounds to keep it simple. Mandarin is not written using an alphabet, but by various strokes (such as —, ┃). Written Chinese is based on these 'characters' rather than words. However, the good news for beginners is that the standard Chinese pronunciation system called 'pinyin' is based on consonants and vowels which look just like English words. By converting a pinyin character (each representing the sound of the Chinese character) into the standard Latin phonetic sound, English/European language speakers will be able to pronounce pinyin easily.

The system of conversion is as follows:

Consonants

Pinyin	Phonetic sound	Converting example
b, d, f, g, j, l, m, n, p, s, t, w, y	pronounced the same as in English	bǎo→bao (宝, treasure)
c	similar to *ts* in *boots*	cí→tsi (词, word/s)
h	similar to *ch* in Scottish *loch*	hē→he (喝, to drink)
q	similar to *ch* in *chip*	qīng→ching (清, clear)
r	similar to *r* in *red*	rén→ren (人, person/people)
x	similar to letter *c* (like the sound of 'see')	xī→ci (西, west)

| z | like *ds* in *kids* | zāi→dsai (灾, disaster) |

| zh | like *j* in *joke* | zhōng→jong (中, middle) |

Vowels

Pinyin	Phonetic sound	Converting example
a	like *a* in *Zara*	mā→ma (妈, mum)
e	like *e* in *her* without the sound of *r*	hē→he (喝, to drink)
i	like *ee* in *bee*	mǐ→mi (米, rice)
o	like the sound of *war*	wǒ→war (我, I/me)
u	like *oo* in s*poon*	lù→loo (路, road)
ü	like the sound of *u*, followed by *ee* in *bee*	ǜ→chu-ee (去, to go)
ai	like the sound of *I*	ài→I (爱, love)
ei	like the sound of letter *a*	měi→may (美, beautiful)
ao	like *ou* in *ouch*	lǎo→lou (老, old)

Pronouncing Mandarin

There are five tones used when pronouncing Mandarin; to make it easier for you to remember them, we have placed the diacritics on top of the vowel in each pinyin to indicate the flat tone (¯), the rising tone (´), the musical long tone (ˇ), the strong tone (`) whilst no diacritic means a quiet tone.

In order to make it easier for you to understand these tones, the following examples are supplied. These will give you some idea of how to pronounce the four basic tones in Mandarin:

Pinyin	English sound
mā	pronounced like 'ma' in the second syllable of 'marmalade'
má	pronounced like 'ma' in 'mass' but with a slightly rising tone
mǎ	pronounced like 'mar' in 'marquee' but holding this sound for slightly longer
mà	pronounced like 'mar' in the first syllable of 'marmalade'

Everyday Photoguide

Everyday China

Open

Push

No Smoking There is no law in China banning smoking in public, but it is widely considered impolite to do so.

Closed

Pull

Emergency Entrance In major cities there are several good clinics catering for tourists.

Litter Bin Rubbish bins are widely available on the streets. There are fines for littering.

Emergency Exit

Reception

Money The Renminbi (RMB) is the currency of China. The Chinese character for RMB is 元 or 圆 **yuán**. One yuan is divided into 10 jiao (角 **jiǎo**) or colloquially mao (毛 **mǎo**). It also breaks down into 100 RMB cents (分 **fēn**). Notes are 1 ¥, 2 ¥, 5 ¥, 10 ¥, 20 ¥, 50 ¥ and 100 ¥. Coins are 1 cent, 2 cents, 5 cents, 10 cent or 1 mao, 50 cent or 5 mao. Most large department stores in China also take both Visa and MasterCard.

ATMs 自动柜员机 are widely available. You can carry out transactions in English and save time queuing in banks. Most ATMs in China accept major credit cards such as Visa and MasterCard. A fee may apply.

24 Hours Self-Service Bank You can withdraw or deposit cash there.

Disabled Parking No cars or bikes.

Chinese Toilet Western-style toilets are usually available in larger cities like Beijing and Shanghai, in hotels and on airplanes. Elsewhere toilets are usually Chinese crouch-over style so be prepared.

China has started star-rating their toilets similar to hotels. Most public toilets charge a fee and often toilet paper isn't provided. Make sure you carry change and some tissue paper with you. You can also buy toilet tissue at the entrance where you pay the fee – ask for 'shǒu zhǐ' (手纸).

Gents Toilet

Police station If you loose your passport or have property stolen you should report it here first. They will issue you with a report certificate.

Ladies Toilet

Opening Hours Banks usually open from 9am to 5/6pm.

Emergency Vehicle You can call free on **120** in any city in China for one of these vehicles to take you to the nearest hospital.

Cross-Over Bridge There are many cross-over bridges as well as cross-under tunnels in the bigger cities. These are the safest ways to cross busy streets.

Cycle Path

Disabled Lift This is reserved for disabled people as well as the elderly, people with young children and pregnant women.

Pedestrian Crossing

No Naked Flames This sign is usually seen in petrol stations.

Budget Hotels still offer a quality service. It is the counterpart of 'Ibis' in the west.

凭票参观
VISIT BY TICKET ONLY

Most cultural heritage sites are not free. You have to buy a ticket to visit them.

保护文物
请勿吸烟
NO SMOKING

Smoking is not allowed in cultural heritage sites.

今日房价
ROOM PRICE

豪华标准房	260
三人房	220
标准房	180
单人房	130
普通双人房	100
普通房	70

Hotel Price List Prices displayed are: deluxe 260 RMB, triple room 220 RMB, standard two-person room 180 RMB, single 130 RMB, smaller two-person room 100 RMB, smaller single 70 RMB.

前方学校

School Sign You need to slow down and look out for children crossing.

社区便民商店

Convenience Store Most towns have a convenience store which stays open 24 hours and offers free delivery to customers who live nearby. These shops often sell phonecards.

图书报刊
BOOKS&NEWSPAPERS

Bookshop In larger cities, signs are in both Chinese and English.

洗　衣　店

Laundry Service Common in big cities. You can have your cleaned clothes back within 2 to 3 days.

道路施工

Road Under Construction

Timetables

日		**Days**
星期一	xīng-qī-yī	Monday
星期二	xīng-qīng-ér	Tuesday
星期三	xīng-qīng-sān	Wednesday
星期四	xīng-qīng-sì	Thursday
星期五	xīng-qīng-wǔ	Friday
星期六	xīng-qīng-liù	Saturday
星期日 (天)	xīng-qīng-rì(tiān)	Sunday

月		**Months**
一月	yī-yüè	January
二月	èr-yüè	February
三月	sān-yüè	March
四月	sì-yüè	April
五月	wǔ-yüè	May
六月	liù-yüè	June
七月	qī-yüè	July
八月	bā-yüè	August
九月	jiǔ-yüè	September
十月	shí-yüè	October
十一月	shí-yī-yüè	November
十二月	shí-èr-yüè	December

Underground Timetable The current station is printed in red. The board shows the destinations and journey's length in minutes.

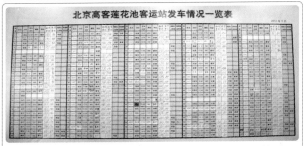

Bus Timetable This platform board in the bus station shows the time, the destination and the price for each bus route.

Tickets

Metro Ticket costs 3 ¥.

Bus Ticket costs 1 ¥.

Non-Contact Card
The cheapest and most convenient way to use public transport. It can be purchased at the station and used for all bus and underground services.

Tickets

Departing city   Train number   Destination city

Ticket price | Valid for 3 days | Departure date and time | Car number and seat

Train Ticket
There is only one national company – China Railway. You can get timetable information at **www.travelchinaguide.com/china-trains.** For local and long distance trains for Hong Kong see **www.kcrc.com**.

Getting around

Buses in big cities are self-service and no change is given, so be prepared. Pay at the front as you enter and exit via the back door. You can also use the non-contact cards. These function as the London Oyster card and are much cheaper and more convenient.

Route Table Often on display at bus stops. These show start and end destinations and all stops in between. An arrow points to where you are on the route. Have someone write down where you want to go to in Chinese characters so that you can recognize it on the board.

Route Number And Destination In larger cities different bus services provide different standards of travel. The price can vary a lot depending on the level of comfort, but will still be much cheaper than a taxi.

Card Reader If the journey is a set-price, you only need to wave your card once before the card reader. A beep means the transaction has been completed successfully. If the bus has different rates, you have to wave your card both when you get on and when you get off.

Subway Station Sign The subway is the quickest and easiest method of transport in large cities such as Beijing, Shanghai and Guangzhou.

Beijing Subway Entrance

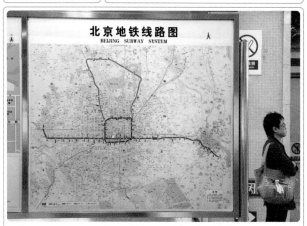

Subway Route Map It would be useful to familiarise yourself with the Chinese characters for the names of the stations. Each station will be announced in both Chinese and English but it would be wise to double check the name with the character.

北京西站各次列车候车地点

车次	候车室	车次	候车室	车次	候车室	车次	候车室	车次	候车室	车次	候车室	车次	候车室	车次	候车室	车次	候车室
Z3	7	T27	6	T97	2	T525	5	K185	6	N203	8	A335	8	1625	8	4443	2
Z11	9	T29	6	T107	6	K21	4	K217	2	N205	2	1363	8	2085	5	4447	4
Z17	5	T41	6	T145	8	K49	5	K219	9	N207	9	1389	7	2089	9	4487	6
Z19	2	T43	5	T151	5	K89	4	K255	9	N213	7	1409	6	2141	8	7095	5
Z37	5	T55	8	T167	2	K105	6	K257	5	N215	9	1427	7	2143	2	7197	9
Z77	8	T57	7	T231	8	K117	5	K261	6	N275	7	1453	9	2163	4	7201	3
T1	5	T61	9	T511	9	K133	7	K267	5	N277	4	1481	3	2519	9	7205	5

Train Departure Board This board gives the train number and the lounge number in which to wait (similar to boarding gates at an airport).

售 站 台 票
SELL PLATFORM TICKET

Platform Ticket Sales If you want to pick up or see someone off from the platform, you have to buy a ticket.

进 站 口 →
ENTRANCE

Station Entrance Your luggage will usually be checked before you enter the train station.

 小红帽行李搬运
P O R T E R

Porter Service is available in larger airports and train stations. Get a price first. There is no need to tip extra.

第三候车室
WAITING LOUNGE No.3 →

Railway Waiting Lounge

计时休息

In some airports and train stations there are more comfortable waiting lounges, which usually charge by the hour.

 车站行李寄存处
STATION BAGGAGE CHECKROOM

Left Luggage In large train stations, you can leave your bags for a few days.

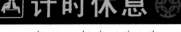

Taxi Meter These are widely used and you can get a receipt at the end of your journey. Try to get your destination written down as most taxi drivers don't speak English.

Taxis are two-tone – different colours for different companies. If the sign on top is lit the taxi is empty. You pay the fee according to the meter. Tipping is not necessary.

Taxi Stand Taxis can't stop wherever they want – if there's a solid white line and its busy, with police around, they're likely to ignore you when you try to hail them down. Try a side street or look for a taxi stand like this where they can pick up and drop off passengers. If you know which way you want to go, it helps to catch the taxi on the right side of the road.

Driving

Parking Entrance
If the car park is not self-service, you are given a slip recording your entrance time, which will be used to calculate the fee when you leave.

Parking Exit
Pay your fee here.

Parking Charges Day time (7am–9pm): small vehicles 1 RMB for half an hour, large vehicles 2 RMB for half an hour
Night time (9pm–7am):
small vehicles 1 RMB for two hours, large vehicles 2 RMB for two hours
Seasonal price: small vehicles 150 RMB per month, 1600 RMB per year. Large vehicles 210 RMB per month, 2300 RMB per year.

If it's a self-service car park, you wave your card here to pay the fee.

You cannot park here between 7am and 6pm. If you break the law your car will be removed by the police.

Car Park Exit
Some car parks operate a one-way traffic system. Follow this exit sign.

Road Ahead For Cars And Bikes

No Bicycles, Motor Vehicles Only

Road Merging Ahead You drive on the right in China.

No Stopping (clear way)

Give Way

Motorway Police The notice board displays the telephone number to call when reporting an accident.

Give Way To Vehicles Turning Right

Motorway Sign Overhead sign on motorway giving information about exit junctions ahead.

Sign showing speed limits for motorway lanes. Red circle indicates maximum speed allowed. Blue circle is the recommended speed.

Motorway Exit

Motorway Toll

U-turns Allowed Except For Buses

Petrol Stations are usually red in China and they are generally manned. The figures on the board (97,93 etc.) refer to octanes.

Shopping

Shopping Centre
There are many discount shopping malls, the counterparts of big-discount retailers such as Carrefour or Walmart.

Chinese Pharmacy
Medical costs are surprisingly low in China but many Western medicines are not available.

Discount Store
for clothing. Use your bargaining skills to pick up designer t-shirts etc. here.

Shopping

Supermarket checkout Signs in larger supermarkets are often in English as well as Chinese. There is the same variety of goods you would expect to find at home.

Mineral Water
is widely available in most shops.

Child Label
showing age group suitability.

Photographic Shop

Biscuits bean pudding thin crisps. There are many varieties of biscuits to choose from mainly made from wheat and rice.

Nutrition Label
These details are supplied on most items. Here there are 6 bags, 30g each. The calories are 113, protein 3g, fat 9g, hydrocarbon 5g sodium 300mg.

In the supermarket, many items are shrink-wrapped and there is no need to weigh or put on a price label.

24

Chinese Folk Toys These are widely available and make lovely souvenirs. They combine Chinese artistic appreciation with play, and the stories usually express people's wish for a happy and contented life. Shadow play is an ancient form of storytelling which uses figures in front of an illuminated backdrop to create an illusion of movement.

Traditional Jewellery Shop
Jade is more important in Chinese culture than diamonds or gold. To buy a really good quality jade article, look for brightness of colour, luster and delicacy of craftwork.

Traditional Chinese Garments Hàn Fú (汉服) is a kind of full-length, one-piece robe which links the **Yī** (衣) and **Shǎng** (裳) together to wrap up the body. It is cut separately but sewn together.

Shu Brocade uses red as it's main colour and has a variety of usually flowery designs. There are four major embroidery styles: **Su**, **Shu**, **Xiang**, and **Yue**. The Chinese word for embroidery is **xìu** and implies beauty and magnificence.

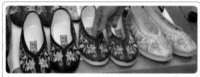

Chinese Shoes China uses European sizes. In China there are various shoe-related customs and wedding shoes have played an important role since ancient times.

Dough Figurines And Chinese Knots Dough figurines (**mianhua** or **miansu**), have a history of some 4,000 years. Usually sold by folk artists in cities like Beijing and Tianjin. Although seemingly outdated, these small figurines still fascinate many children. Chinese knots have also been a popular gift for thousands of years and embodies best wishes. First used as a decorative addition to clothing and later to decorate their houses.

Keeping in touch

Post Offices in China are green. You can send your letters, parcels, or make phone calls here.

Post Box If there are two slits, one is for local mail, the other is for everywhere else. Collection times are indicated on the front.

This is a SIM card for 'pay as you go'. There are two mobile operators – **China Mobil** and **China Unicom** – both have a network which covers the whole of China.

Internet Café There are many internet cafés in China. They charge by the hour. Some have microphones, earphones and webcams available. These can be used to video chat using MSN, Yahoo messenger or Skype.

Public Telephone services are manned in China. Payment is calculated for the duration of the call, recorded on a meter. Phone cards are available for cheap international calls. You dial a number, then follow the voice guide, which is in both English and Chinese, to make the call. It is usually 60% cheaper than a direct call.

Key talk

Key talk

• It is very important to use the appropriate way of greeting in China. How you greet somebody depends on whether you know them or they are strangers. The most popular greeting is 你好 (nǐ hǎo), which can be used at anytime, to anybody.

• Another greeting word is 您好 (nín hǎo), it is more formal and always used when you want to show particular respect.

yes	是	shì
no	不是	bùshì
OK!	好!	hǎo!
please	请	qǐng
thanks	谢谢	xièxie
thank you very much	非常感谢	fēicháng gǎnxiè
you're welcome!	不客气!	bù kèqì!
yes, please	好, 谢谢	hǎo, xièxie
no, thanks	不, 谢谢	bù, xièxie
hello	你好	nǐhǎo
hello! (on the phone)	喂!	wèi!
hi!	嗨!	hāi!
bye!	再会!	zàihuì!
goodbye	再见	zàijiàn
good morning!	早上好!	zǎoshang hǎo!
morning!	早!	zǎo!
good evening	晚上好	wǎnshang hǎo
goodnight	晚安	wǎn ān
excuse me!/sorry!	对不起!	duìbùqǐ!

excuse me! (to get past in a crowd)	请让一让！
	qǐng ràngyīràng!
I'd like...	我想…
	wǒ xiǎng...
a coffee please	请给我一杯咖啡
	qǐng gěiwǒ yībēi kāfēi
a beer please	请给我一杯啤酒
	qǐng gěiwǒ yībēi píjiǔ
we'd like...	我们想…
	wǒmen xiǎng...
two coffees please	请给我两杯咖啡
	qǐng gěiwǒ liǎngbēi kāfēi
two beers please	请给我两杯啤酒
	qǐng gěiwǒ liǎngbēi píjiǔ
a coffee and two beers please	请给我一杯咖啡两杯啤酒
	qǐng gěiwǒ yībēi kāfēi liǎngbēi píjiǔ
I'd like an ice cream	我想买一个冰淇淋
	wǒ xiǎng mǎi yīgè bīngqílín
we'd like to go home	我们想回家
	wǒmen xiǎng huíjiā
another/some more...	另外的/更多的…
	lìngwàide/gèngduōde...
do you have...?	你（们）有 … 吗？
	nǐ(men) yǒu … ma?
do you have a room?	你（们）有客房吗？
	nǐ(men) yǒu kèfáng ma?
do you have milk?	你（们）有牛奶吗？
	nǐ(men) yǒu niúnǎi ma?
do you have any stamps?	你（们）有邮票吗？
	nǐ(men) yǒu yóupiào ma?
do you have a map?	你（们）有地图吗？
	nǐ(men) yǒu dìtú ma?
how much is it?	多少钱？
	duōshǎo qián

how much is the room for one night?	这间房住一晚多少钱? zhè jiānfáng zhù yīwǎn duōshǎo qián?
how much is a ticket?	一张票多少钱? yīzhāngpiào duōshǎo qián?
how much is each one?	每个多少钱? měigè duōshǎo qián?
how much is a kilogram?	多少钱一公斤? duōshǎo qián yī gōngjīn?
where is...?/ where are...?	…在哪儿? …zài nǎr?
where is the bus station?	汽车站在哪儿? qìchēzhàn zài nǎr?
where are the toilets?	厕所在哪儿? cèsuǒ zài nǎr?
how do I get...?	我怎么去…? wǒ zěnme qù…?
to the museum	去博物馆 qù bówùguǎn
to the bus station	去车站 qù chēzhàn
to Shanghai	去上海 qù shànghǎi
is there/ are there...?	有没有…? yǒu méi yǒu…?
there is.../ there are...	有… yǒu…
there isn't.../ there aren't any...	没有… méiyǒu…
is there a restaurant?	有餐馆吗? yǒu cānguǎn ma?
is there a pharmacy?	有药店吗? yǒu yàodiàn ma?
is there a swimming pool?	有游泳池吗? yǒu yóuyǒngchí ma?

there is no hot water	没有热水
	méiyǒu rèshuǐ
there are no towels	没有毛巾
	méiyǒu máojīn
I need...	我需要···
	wǒ xūyào...
I need a taxi	我需要一辆出租车
	wǒ xūyào yīliàng chūzū chē
I need to send a fax	我需要发一份传真
	wǒ xūyào fā yīfèn chuán zhēn
can I...?	我能 ··· 吗？
	wǒ néng ... ma?
can we...?	我们能 ··· 吗？
	wǒmen néng ... ma?
can I pay?	我可以付钱吗？
	wǒ kěyǐ fùqián ma?
can we go in?	我可以进去吗？
	wǒ kěyǐ jìnqù ma?
where can I...?	我能在哪儿···？
	wǒ néng zài nǎr...?
where can I buy bread?	我能在哪儿买到面包？
	wǒ néng zài nǎr mǎi dào miànbāo?
where can I hire bikes?	我能在哪儿租到自行车？
	wǒ néng zài nǎr zū dào zìxíngchē?
when?	什么时候？
	shénme shíhou?
at what time...?	什么时间···？
	shénme shíjiān...?
when is breakfast?	什么时候吃早餐？
	shénme shíhou chī zǎocān?
when is dinner?	什么时候吃晚饭？
	shénme shíhou chī wǎnfàn?
when does it open/close?	什么时候开/关门？
	shénme shíhou kāi/guānmén?

when does it begin/finish?	什么时候开始/结束?
	shénme shíhou kāishǐ/jiéshù?
yesterday	昨天
	zuótiān
today	今天
	jīntiān
tomorrow	明天
	míngtiān
this morning	今天早上
	jīntiān zǎoshàng
this afternoon	今天下午
	jīntiān xiàwǔ
tonight	今天晚上
	jīntiān wǎnshàng
is it open?	开门了吗?
	kāimén le ma?
is it closed?	关门了吗?
	guānmén le ma?
Sir/Mr...	···先生
	...xiānsheng
Madam/Ms...	···女士
	...nǔshì
Mrs...	···太太
	...tàitai
Miss...	···小姐
	...xiǎojiě
how are you?	你好吗?
	nǐ hǎo ma?
how have you been?	最近身体怎么样?
	zuìjin shēntǐ zěnmeyàng?
fine, thanks	好, 谢谢
	hǎo, xièxie
great!	棒极了!
	bàng jí le!

so-so 一般
yībān

and you? 你呢?
nǐ ne?

my name is... 我叫…
wǒ jiào…

what's your name? 你叫什么名字?
nǐ jiào shénme míngzi?

I don't understand 我不明白
wǒ bù míngbai

I don't speak 我不会说普通话
  Mandarin wǒ bù huì shuō pǔtōnghuà

do you understand? 你明白了吗?
nǐ míngbai le ma?

do you speak 你会说英语吗?
  English? nǐ huì shuō yīngyǔ ma?

long time no see! 好久不见！最近还好吗?
  how are you hǎojiǔ bù jiàn! zuìjìn hái hǎo ma?
  doing?

see you later 一会儿见
yīhuìr jiàn

see you at seven 7点见
qīdiǎn jiàn

see you on Monday! 星期一见！
xīngqīyī jiàn!

see you tomorrow 明天见
míngtiān jiàn

• In China, family names are placed first, followed by the given name. For instance in the name 'Zhao Li,' 'Zhao' is the family name and 'Li' the given name. The family name usually consists of one syllable, whereas the given name can have either one or two syllables.

• Chinese people call their close friends and family members by their given names. For example, 'Ma Wenli' may be addressed by close friends as 'Wenli.'

what's your name?	你叫什么名字?
	nǐ jiào shénme míngzi?
my name is...	我叫…
	wǒ jiào…
where are you from?	你是哪里人?
	nǐ shì nǎli rén?
I am English, from London	我是英国人, 我来自伦敦
	wǒ shì yīngguórén, wǒ lái zì lúndūn
nice to meet you!	很高兴认识你!
	hěn gāoxìng rènshi nǐ!
how old are you?	你多大了?
	nǐ duōdà le?
I'm ... years old	我 … 岁了
	wǒ … suì le
where do you live?	你住在哪儿?
	nǐ zhùzài nǎr?
I live in London	我住在伦敦
	wǒ zhùzài lúndūn
where do you live? (plural)	你们住在哪儿?
	nǐmen zhùzài nǎr?
we live in Glasgow	我们住在格拉斯哥
	wǒmen zhùzài gélāsīgē
I'm at school	我在上学
	wǒ zài shàngxué
I work	我在工作
	wǒ zài gōngzuò

I'm retired	我退休了
	wǒ tuìxiū le
I'm...	我…
	wǒ...
single	单身
	dānshēn
married	结婚了
	jiéhūn le
divorced	离婚了
	líhūn le
I have...	我有…
	wǒ yǒu...
a boyfriend	一位男朋友
	yīwèi nánpéngyou
a girlfriend	一位女朋友
	yīwèi nǔpéngyou
a partner	一位伴侣
	yīwèi bànlǚ
I have four children	我有四个孩子
	wǒ yǒu sìgè háizi
I have no children	我没有孩子
	wǒ méiyǒu háizi
let me introduce you to my friends	让我把你介绍给我的朋友们
	ràng wǒ bǎ nǐ jièshào gěi wǒ de péngyoumen
I'd like you to meet my husband	我想让你认识一下我的丈夫
	wǒ xiǎng ràng nǐ rènshi yīxià wǒ de zhàngfu
please allow me to introduce these distinguished guests	请允许我介绍一下到场的嘉宾
	qǐng yǔnxǔ wǒ jièshào yīxià dàochǎng de jiābīn
this is Janet	这是珍妮特
	zhè shì Zhēnnítè

I'm here...	我在这里…
	wǒ zài zhèlǐ...
on holiday	度假
	dùjià
on business	出差
	chūchāi
for the weekend	过周末
	guò zhōumò

Money

Money – changing

- The Renminbi is the currency in China. The units of Renminbi are 元 (yuán), 角 (jiǎo) and 分 (fēn).
- Cash machines (ATMs) are know as 自动柜员机 and are widely available in major cities. You can carry out the transaction in English and save time queuing in banks.
- You can withdraw cash, free of charge, from any ATM with the 银联 logo, but you may be subject to a charge from your card issuer.
- Most cash machines accept Visa and Mastercard.
- Major currencies can be exchanged at banks, top-end hotels and some large department stores. The rate offered is usually the official rate, so there's little point in shopping around. It is illegal (and risky!) to exchange money outside of the banking system.
- When you exchange money, keep the receipt. You will need it if you want to change back any spare RMB you have left at the end of your trip.

where can I change some money?	我在哪儿能换钱?
	wǒ zài nǎr néng huànqián?
where is the bank?	银行在哪儿?
	yínháng zài nǎr?
when does the bank open?	银行什么时间开门?
	yínháng shénme shíjiān kāimén?
when does the bank close?	银行什么时间关门?
	yínháng shénme shíjiān guānmén?

where is the nearest bureau de change?	最近的外汇兑换局在哪儿?
	zuì jìn de wàihuì duìhuàn jú zài nǎr?
what is the rate for...?	…的汇率是多少?
	…de huìlǜ shì duōshǎo?
I want to change these traveller's cheques	我想兑现这些旅行支票
	wǒ xiǎng duìxiàn zhè xiē lǚxíngzhīpiào
where is the nearest cash machine?	离这儿最近的取钞机在哪儿?
	lí zhèr zuìjìn de qǔchāojī zàinǎr?
can I use my credit card at the cash machine?	我能使用信用卡从取钞机取钞吗?
	wǒ néng shǐyòng xìnyòngkǎ cóng qǔchāojī qǔchāo ma?
do you have any loose change?	你有零钱吗?
	nǐ yǒu língqián ma?

Money – spending

- UK visitors should note that Scottish and Northern Ireland bank notes are NOT accepted.
- You can use your bank card as you would at home to withdraw cash or pay at shops.
- Outside major cities and tourist areas, credit cards are not always readily acceptable and the availability of cash machines (ATMs) can be limited.

how much is it?	多少钱?
	duōshǎo qián?
how much will it be?	大概要付多少钱?
	dàgài yào fù duōshǎo qián?
can I pay with euros?	我可以用欧元付款吗?
	wǒ kěyǐ yòng ōuyuán fùkuǎn ma?

can I pay by ... credit card/ cheque?	我可以使用信用卡/支票付款吗? wǒ kěyǐ shǐyòng xìnyòngkǎ/zhīpiào fùkuǎn ma?
is service included?	服务费已经包括在内了吗? fúwùfèi yǐjīng bāokuò zài nèi le ma?
put it on my bill	请加在我的帐单上 qǐng jiā zài wǒ de zhàngdān shàng
where do I pay?	我在哪儿付款? wǒ zài nǎr fùkuǎn?
I need a receipt, please	请给我一张收据 qǐng gěi wǒ yī zhāng shōujù
do I pay in advance?	我需要预先付款吗? wǒ xūyào yùxiān fùkuǎn ma?
do I need to pay a deposit?	我需要先付定金吗? wǒ xūyào xiānfù dìngjīn ma?
I'm sorry	对不起 duìbùqǐ
I've nothing smaller (no change)	我没有零钱 wǒ méiyǒu língqián

Getting around

Airport

• Airport announcements are generally in English as well as Chinese.
• Some airports have VIP lounges which are charged by the hour.
• You will find porter service in most large airports. You should ask the price first – there is no need to tip on top of the price given.
• Most airlines and airports in China provide facilities for disabled travellers and infants. Ask the staff for assistance if you are having difficulties.

how do I get to the airport?	我怎么去机场?
	wǒ zěnme qù jīchǎng?
is there a bus to the airport?	有公共汽车去机场吗?
	yǒu gōnggòngqìchē qù jīchǎng ma?
where do I get the bus into town?	我在哪儿坐去市中心的公共汽车?
	wǒ zài nǎr zuò qù shìzhōngxīn de gōnggòngqìchē?
where is the train to...?	去 ··· 的火车在哪里?
	qù ... de huǒchē zài nǎli?
where is the luggage for the flight from...?	来自 ··· 航班的行李在哪里?
	láizì ... hángbānde xíngli zài nǎli?
where is the information desk?	服务台在哪里?
	fúwùtái zài nǎli?
where is the check-in desk for...?	登记处在哪里?
	dēngjìchù zài nǎli?

how much is it to go to ... by taxi?	搭乘出租车去 … 要多少钱?
	dāchéng chūzūchē qù … yào duōshǎo qián?
boarding will take place at gate 5	请在5号登机口登机
	qǐng zài 5 hào dēngjīkǒu dēngjī
go immediately to gate 5	请迅速去5号登机口
	qǐng xùnsù qù 5 hào dēngjīkǒu

Customers and passports

● A valid passport and tourist visa are required by all non-Chinese nationals wishing to enter mainland China.
● You need to fill in a health declaration certificate and customs claim form on arrival.
● Check the validity of your visa carefully as fines can be levied for overstaying.
● Only the British Embassy in Beijing can issue replacement passports (report the loss first to the nearest police station).

I have nothing to declare	我没有要申报的物品
	wǒ méiyǒu yào shēnbào de wùpǐn
here is...	这是…
	zhè shì...
my passport	我的护照
	wǒde hùzhào
my visa	我的签证
	wǒ de qiānzhèng
do I have to pay duty on this?	我要支付这商品的关税吗?
	wǒ yào zhīfù zhè shāngpǐn de guānshuì ma?
it's for my own personal use/ for a present	这是我自用的/送人的礼品
	zhè shì wǒ zìyòngde/sòngrénde lǐpǐn

here is the receipt	这是收据 zhè shì shōujù
I am here on holiday/business	我在这里度假/出差 wǒ zài zhèlǐ dùjià/chūchāi
we are on our way to... (if in transit through a country)	我们正在转机去⋯ wǒmen zhèngzài zhuǎnjī qù...
the child's name is on this passport	孩子的名字在这本护照上 háizi de míngzi zài zhè běn hùzhào shàng
this is the baby's passport	这是婴儿的护照 zhèshì yīngér de hùzhào

Asking the way – questions

- If you want to ask a stranger something when you are on a street, start with 你好，请问⋯ (nǐ hǎo, qǐng wèn)
- Younger people are more likely to speak English, so approach them first when you are looking for directions.

excuse me!	请问一下 qǐng wèn yī xià
where is/are...?	⋯在哪儿? ...zài nǎr?
where is the nearest supermarket?	离这儿最近的超市在哪里? lí zhèr zuìjìnde chāoshì zài nǎlǐ?
how do I/we get...	我/我们怎么⋯ wǒ/wǒmen zěnme...
onto the motorway?	上高速公路? shàng gāosùgōnglù?
to the museum?	去博物馆? qù bówùguǎn?

to the shops?	去商店
	qù shāngdiàn?
excuse me, how do I get to the station?	请问, 我怎么去车站?
	qǐngwèn, wǒ zěnme qù chēzhàn?
is it far?	远吗?
	yuǎn ma?
can I/we walk there?	我/我们可以步行去那里吗?
	wǒ/wǒmen kěyǐ bùxíng qù nàli ma?
we're looking for...	我们正在找···
	wǒmen zhèngzài zhǎo...
is this the right way to...?	这是去 ··· 的路吗?
	zhèshì qù ... delù ma?
we're lost	我们迷路了
	wǒmen mílù le
can you show me on the map?	你能在地图上指给我看吗?
	nǐ néng zài dìtú shàng zhǐ gěi wǒ kàn ma?

Asking the way – answers

● You will find Chinese people very friendly and eager to help if you are lost.

● When travelling by bus or taxi it is better to write down your destination in Chinese and take a map with you. Someone Chinese may not recognize a place name if your pronunciation is not accurate. It is easier for them to show you the direction on a map.

no, this is not the way to...	不, 这不是去 ··· 的路
	bù, zhè búshì qù ... de lù
keep going straight ahead	一直往前走
	yīzhí wǎng qián zǒu
as far as...	直道···
	zhí dào...

you have to turn round	你要拐弯 nǐ yào guǎiwān
turn right/left	向右/左转 xiàng yòu/zuǒ zhuǎn
go towards the church	朝教堂的方向走 cháo jiào táng de fāng xiàng zǒu
take the first on the right	第一个路口右转 dì yīgè lùkǒu yòuzhuǎn
follow the signs for...	跟着 ⋯ 的标记走 gēn zhe … de biāojì zǒu
there, on the right	那里, 在右边 nàlǐ, zài yòubiān
keep straight on, after the church turn left/right	一直往前走, 过了教堂就往左/右拐 yīzhí wǎng qián zǒu, guòle jiàotáng jiù wǎng zuǒ/yòu guǎi
opposite	对面的 duìmiànde
next to	旁边的 pángbiānde
near to	邻近 línjìn
traffic lights	红绿灯 hónglǜdēng
crossroads	十字路口 shízìlùkǒu
corner (of road)	(路)边 (lù)biān
down there	在那里 zài nàlǐ
behind	在后面 zài hòumiàn
then ask again	然后再问人 ránhòu zài wèn rén

Bus and coach

• •

• Buses are very cheap but are normally crowded, stuffy and slow during peak times. In larger cities, some routes have new super-buses that are more expensive, but have comfortable seating and air conditioning.

• Buses in cities such as Beijing and Shanghai are usually self-service. You must have the correct money ready for the machine near the bus driver.

• Non-contact cards, similar to the London Oyster card, are much cheaper and more convenient. You can use them for all bus journeys and the metro.

• Bus stops often have route tables. Have someone write down your destination so you can recognize it on the board.

• You can reach most of China by bus. In Beijing and Shanghai, there are 4 or 5 long distance bus companies each covering different areas. Liuliqiao bus station (in Beijing) is for buses going west – Zhaogongcun is for buses going in an easterly direction.

44

excuse me, which bus goes to the city/town centre?	请问, 哪辆公共汽车去市/镇中心? qǐngwèn, nǎ liàng gōnggòngqìchē qù shì/zhèn zhōngxīn?
where is the bus stop?	公共汽车站在哪里? gōnggòngqìchēzhàn zài nǎli?
where can I buy the tickets?	我在哪里买车票? wǒ zài nǎli mǎi chēpiào?
is there a bus to...?	有去 … 的公共汽车吗? yǒu qù … de gōnggòngqìchēma?
is there a tram to...?	有电车去 … 吗? yǒu diànchē qù … ma?
where do I catch the bus to...?	我在哪里搭乘去 … 的公共汽车? wǒ zài nǎli dāchéng qù … de gōng gòngqìchē?

where do I catch the tram to...?	我在哪里搭乘去 ⋯ 的电车?
	wǒ zài nǎli dāchéng qù … de diànchē?
how much is it to go...?	去 ⋯ 要多少钱?
	qù … yào duōshǎo qián?
to the city/town centre	去市/镇中心
	qù shì/zhèn zhōngxīn
how often are the buses to...?	每隔多长时间就有一班公共汽车去…?
	měi gé duōcháng shíjiān jiù yǒu yībān gōnggòngqìchē qù…?
when is the first/ the last bus to...?	去 ⋯ 的第一班/最后一班公共汽车是什么时间?
	qù … de dìyībān/zuìhòuyībān gōng gòngqìchē shì shénme shíjiān?
please tell me when to get off	到时候请您告诉我下车
	dào shíhou qǐng nín gàosù wǒ xiàchē
this is your stop	你在这一站下车
	nǐ zài zhèyīzhàn xiàchē
please let me off	请让我下车
	qǐng ràng wǒ xiàchē
this is my stop	我要在这一站下车
	wǒ yào zài zhèyīzhàn xiàchē
take the metro, it's quicker	坐地铁要快些
	zuò dìtiě yào kuàixiē

Metro

• •

• Shanghai and Beijing have good metro systems. Guangzhou has a basic system but new lines are constantly being added.
• If the Chinese city you are visiting has an underground system, it's a good idea to use it as it's going to be faster than a taxi or bus on the usually gridlocked streets.
• Tickets can be purchased from the ticket offices above the platforms and you can also use non-contact cards, which are much cheaper.
• Signs and announcements are in both Chinese and English.

a 24-hour ticket	一张24小时内使用的车票 yīzhāng èrshísì xiǎoshí nèi shǐyòng de chēpiào
a 48-hour ticket	一张48小时内使用的车票 yīzhāng sìshíbā xiǎoshí nèi shǐyòng de chēpiào
where is the nearest metro?	离这儿最近的地铁站在哪里? lí zhèr zuìjìnde dìtiězhàn zàinǎli?
how does the ticket machine work?	如何使用售票机? rúhé shǐyòng shòupiàojī?
do you have a map of the metro?	你有一张地铁图吗? nǐ yǒu yīzhāng dìtiětú ma?
how do I get to...?	我怎么去…? wǒ zěnme qù...?
do I have to change?	我要换车吗? wǒ yào huànchē ma?
what is the next stop?	下一站是哪一站? xiàyīzhàn shì nǎyīzhàn?
this is my stop	我要在这一站下车 wǒ yào zài zhèyīzhàn xiàchē
please let me out	请让我出去 qǐng ràng wǒ chūqù

Train

• Trains link virtually all main cities and towns in China and are a safe and comfortable way to travel, even for families or women travelling alone.

• They have four classes: soft seat, soft sleeper, hard seat, hard sleeper. Short distance trains normally have only hard class seats.

• Trains starting with the letter 'T' are express trains, similar to ICE in Europe.

• Arrive at the station in plenty of time. In major cities, stations can be large and busy and it may take a while to find your train.

• All major train stations have security checks (including airline-style luggage checks) to go through before boarding.

where is the station?	车站在哪里? chēzhàn zài nǎli?
to the station, please	请去车站 qǐng qù chēzhàn
where is the ticket office?	售票处在哪里? shòupiàochù zài nǎli?
how much does it cost to...?	去 … 多少钱? qù … duōshǎo qián?
a single	一张单程票 yīzhāng dānchéng piào
2 singles	两张单程票 liǎngzhāng dānchéng piào
a child's single	一张儿童单程票 yīzhāng értóng dānchéng piào
a return	一张往返票 yīzhāng wǎngfǎn piào
2 returns	两张往返票 liǎngzhāng wǎngfǎn piào

a child's return	一张儿童往返票
	yīzhāng értóng wǎngfǎn piào
I'd like 3 tickets, please	我想买三张票
	wǒ xiǎng mǎi sān zhāng piào
1 ticket/2 tickets to...	一/两张去 … 的票
	yī/liǎng zhāng qù … de piào
first/second class	头等/二等
	tóuděng/èrděng
smoking/ non-smoking	吸烟/禁烟区
	xīyān/jìnyānqū
is there a supplement to pay?	要付附加费吗?
	yào fù fùjiāfèi ma?
when is the next train to...?	下一趟去 … 的火车是什么时间?
	xiàyītàng qù … de huǒchē shì shénme shíjiān?
do I have to change?	我要换车吗?
	wǒ yào huànchē ma?
which platform does it leave from?	从哪个站台出发?
	cóng nǎgè zhàntái chūfā?
is this the train for...?	这是去 … 的火车吗?
	zhè shì qù … de huǒchē ma?
does it stop at...?	它在 … 停吗?
	tā zài … tíng ma?
when does it arrive in...?	它什么时候到达…?
	tā shénme shíhou dàodá…?
please tell me when we get to...	到达 … 时请告诉我
	dàodá … shí qǐng gàosù wǒ
is there a restaurant car?	有餐车吗?
	yǒu cānchē ma?
is this seat free?	有人坐这个座位吗?
	yǒu rén zuò zhège zuòwèi ma?
excuse me! (to get past)	请让一让!
	qǐng ràngyīràng!

platform	站台
	zhàntái
ticket office	售票处
	shòupiàochù
timetable	时刻表
	shíkèbiǎo
delay (appears on	晚点
train noticeboards)	wǎndiǎn
left luggage	行李暂存
	xíngli zàncún

Taxi

• Taxis in China are cheap and plentiful and, unless there is a metro system, are usually the most convenient way to get around a city.

• A lit sign on top indicates they are available.

• Taxis are not allowed to stop just anywhere and it is often easier to hail them down in a side street or look for a taxi stand.

• Taxis are metered so just pay the fare indicated – normally there is no tipping. The machine will also print out receipts automatically for you if you need them.

• Assume your driver will not speak English and keep the name of your hotel or destination written down in Chinese.

I want a taxi	我想叫一辆出租车
	wǒ xiǎng jiào yīliàng chūzūchē
where can I get a taxi?	我在哪儿可以叫一辆出租车?
	wǒ zài nǎr kěyǐ jiào yīliàng chūzūchē?
please order me a taxi now for... (time)	请现在为我叫一辆 ⋯ 点的出租车
	qǐng xiànzài wèi wǒ jiào yīliàng ... diǎn de chūzūchē
how much will it cost to go to...?	去 ⋯ 要多少钱?
	qù ... yào duōshǎo qián?

the station	车站
	chēzhàn
the airport	机场
	jīchǎng
this address	这个地址
	zhègè dìzhǐ
how much is it?	多少钱?
	duōshǎo qián?
why is it so much?	为什么这么多钱?
	wèishénme zhème duōqián?
it's more than on the meter	收费多于计费表上显示的价钱
	shōufèi duōyú jìfèibiǎo shàng xiǎnshìde jiàqián
keep the change	不用找零钱给我
	bú yòng zhǎo língián gěi wǒ
sorry, I don't have any change	对不起, 我没有零钱
	duìbùqǐ, wǒ méiyǒu língqián
I'm in a hurry	我要赶时间
	wǒ yào gǎn shíjiān
can you go a little faster?	你能开快一些吗?
	nǐ néng kāi kuàiyīxiē ma?
I have to catch...	我要赶…
	wǒ yào gǎn…
a train	一趟火车
	yītàng huǒchē
a plane	一架飞机
	yījià fēijī

Boat and ferry

• All major rivers in China have ferry services and these are generally well equipped to serve tourists. The Yangzi is especially well catered for and there is a good selection of boat trips available.

• River ferries operate between Chongqing, Wuhan, Nanjing and Shanghai. Coastal ferries operate between Dalian, Tianjin (Tientsin), Qingdao (Tsingtao) and Shanghai.

• There are regular ferry services between mainland China and Hong Kong, conditions on which vary.

have you a timetable?	你有一张时刻表吗? nǐ yǒu yīzhāng shíkèbiǎo ma?
is there a car ferry to...?	有去 … 的载轿车的渡轮吗? yǒu qù … de zǎijiàochēde dùlún ma?
how much is a ticket to...?	一张去 … 的票要多少钱? yīzhāng qù … de piào yào duōshǎo qián?
single/return	单程/往返 dānchéng/wǎngfǎn
how much is it for a car and ... people?	一辆轿车和 … 人要多少钱? yīliàng jiàochē hé … rén yào duōshǎo qián?
when is the first boat?	第一班轮船是什么时间? dìyībān lúnchuán shì shénme shíjiān?
when is the last boat?	最后一班轮船是什么时间? zuìhòu yībān lúnchuán shì shénme shíjiān?
this is the last boat	这是最后一班轮船 zhè shì zuìhòu yībān lúnchuán

Car

Driving

• Speed limits in China are 40 km/h in built-up areas, 100 km/h on main roads, and 120 km/h on motorways.
• Driving in China is on the right, but in Hong Kong it is on the left.
• A national motorway system links most major cities around the country. However, most of them are toll motorways.
• Distances should not be underestimated. From Beijing to Shanghai is 1,461 km (908 miles) and from Dandong to Lhasa 4,600 km (3,000 miles). Make sure your vehicle is in good mechanical condition before embarking on a long journey.

where can I park?	我在哪里可以停车?
	wǒ zài nǎli kěyǐ tíng chē?
can I/we park here?	我/我们可以在这里停放车吗?
	wǒ/wǒmen kěyǐ zài zhèlǐ tíngfàng chē ma?
how long for?	可以停放多长时间?
	kěyǐ tíngfàng duōcháng shíjiān?
we're going to...	我们要去…
	wǒmen yào qù…
what's the best route?	哪条路最好?
	nǎtiáo lù zuì hǎo?
how do I get onto the motorway?	我怎样上高速?
	wǒ zěn yàng shàng gāo sù?
which junction is it for...?	去 … 是哪一个出口?
	qù … shì nǎ yīgè chūkǒu?
do I/we need snow chains?	我/我们需要雪链吗?
	wǒ/wǒmen xūyào xuěliàn ma?

Petrol

• Petrol stations in China are usually red. They are generally manned and many only accept cash.
• Some petrol stations have convenience stores as well.

is there a petrol station near here?	附近有加油站吗？ fùjìn yǒu jiāyóuzhàn ma?
fill it up, please	请加满油 qǐng jiāmǎn yóu
100 yuan-worth of unleaded petrol	100元的无铅汽油 yībǎi yuánde wúqiānqìyóu
where is...?	…在哪儿？ …zài nǎr?
the air line/water	充气管/水 chōngqìguǎn/shuǐ
please check the oil	请检查机油 qǐng jiǎnchá jīyóu
please check the water	请检查水 qǐng jiǎnchá shuǐ
pump number...	…号泵 …hàobèng
where do I pay?	我在哪儿付款？ wǒ zài nǎr fùkuǎn?
can I pay by credit card?	我可以使用信用卡付款吗？ wǒ kěyǐ shǐyòng xìnyòngkǎ fùkuǎn ma?
4 star	4星 sìxīng
diesel oil	柴油 cháiyóu
unleaded	无铅汽油 wúqiānqìyóu

you need some oil/some water	你需要一些机油/水
	nǐ xūyào yīxiē jīyóu/shuǐ
everything is OK	一切都好
	yīqiè dōu hǎo

Problems/breakdown

- A garage that does repairs is known as a 修车行 (xiūchēháng).
- Outwith cities, China is still very much an agricultural nation without the mechanical facilities or services found in the West. You can, however, join a car club and take advantage of their emergency rescue service.

can you help me?	你能帮助我吗?
	nǐ néng bāngzhù wǒ ma?
my car has broken down	我的车出了故障
	wǒde chē chūle gùzhàng
I've run out of petrol	我没汽油了
	wǒ méi qìyóu le
I'm on my own	我一个人来的
	wǒ yígèrén lái de
I have children in the car	我的车上有孩子
	wǒde chēshàng yǒu háizi
can you tow me to the nearest garage?	你能把我的车拖到离这儿最近的修车行吗?
	nǐ néng bǎ wǒde chē tuōdào lí zhèr zuìjìnde xiūchēháng ma?
is it serious?	故障严重吗?
	gùzhàng yánzhòng ma?
can you repair it?	你能修好它吗?
	nǐ néng xiū hǎo tā ma?
do you have parts for a (make of car)?	你有 … 车的零件吗?
	nǐ yǒu … chēde língjiàn ma?

there's something wrong with the...	…坏了
	…huàile
can you replace the...?	你能更换 … 吗?
	nǐ néng gēnghuàn … ma?

Car hire

• China has not signed the convention which created International Driving Permits, however travellers from abroad are now able to drive Chinese vehicles following a quick hour-long traffic law briefing. Your license, however, will be time-limited.

• In some cities electric scooters are legally treated as bicycles and you do not need a driver's license to ride them. There may be restrictions as to where you can ride them, i.e. not in the main traffic lanes.

where is the nearest car hire company?	最近的租车公司在哪儿?
	zuìjìn de zūchē gōngsī zài nǎr?
I want to hire a car for ... days	我想租一辆车用 … 天
	wǒ xiǎng zū yīliàng chē yòng … tiān
I would like a small car	我想租一辆小车
	wǒ xiǎng zū yīliàng xiǎochē
I would like a large car	我想租一辆大车
	wǒ xiǎng zū yīliàng dàchē
with automatic gears	自动档
	zìdòngdǎng
what are your rates for...?	你们 … 的收费是多少钱?
	nǐmen … de shōufèi shì duōshǎo qián?
per day	每天
	měitiān
per week	每周
	měizhōu

how much is the deposit?	定金是多少?
	dìngjīn shì duōshǎo?
do you take credit cards?	你们接受信用卡吗?
	nǐmen jiēshòu xìnyòngkǎ ma?
is there a mileage (kilometre) charge?	有按公里数的收费吗?
	yǒu àn gōnglǐ shùde shōufèi ma?
how much is it?	多少钱?
	duōshǎo qián?
does the price include fully comprehensive insurance?	收费包括全保险吗?
	shōufèi bāokuò quán bǎoxiǎn ma?
must I return the car here?	我必须在这里还车吗?
	wǒ bìxū zài zhèlǐ huánchē ma?
by what time?	在什么时间以前?
	zài shénme shíjiān yǐqián?
I'd like to leave it in...	我想把它留在…
	wǒ xiǎng bǎ tā liú zài…
please return the car with a full tank	还车时油箱必须是加满的
	huánchē shí yóuxiāng bìxū shì jiāmǎn de
where is the nearest petrol station?	最近的加油站在哪儿?
	zuì jìn de jiāyóuzhàn zài nǎr?

Shopping

Shopping – holiday

- In China, the opening hours of shopping centres are normally from 9am to 10pm. Some large shops close one hour later during festivals and sale time.
- Banks, hospitals, and post offices usually open every day from 8.30/9am–5.30/6pm. Shops, supermarkets, pharmacies etc are open 7 days a week from 8.30am–8pm, some even have 24 hour opening. Restaurants, bars and clubs stay open till the small hours of the morning.
- You can bargain for almost anything in China. Bargaining is a friendly, social art so don't be shy about stating your price.
- Often what you want is sold at more than one stall in the area so ask prices and bargain at several before buying.
- The Liulichang and Panjiayuan Markets in Beijing are super shopping markets for all Chinese arts and crafts. However, you really need expert advice to discern the true art crafts from the fake.

do you sell...?	这里卖 … 吗?
	zhèlǐ mài … ma?
stamps	邮票
	yóupiào
postcards	明信片
	míngxìnpiàn
10 stamps	10张邮票
	shízhāng yóupiào
four postcards	四张明信片
	sìzhāng míngxìnpiàn

to Britain	寄往英国
	jì wǎng yīngguó
do you have...?	你们有 … 吗?
	nǐmen yǒu … ma?
where can I buy...?	我在哪儿可以买…
	wǒ zài nǎr kěyǐ mǎi…
shoes	鞋子
	xiézi
gifts	礼物
	lǐwù
I'm looking for a present for...	我想为 … 买一份礼物
	wǒ xiǎng wèi … mǎi yī fèn lǐwù
my mother	我的妈妈
	wǒ de māma
a child	一个孩子
	yī gè háizi
have you anything cheaper?	有没有便宜一点的东西?
	yǒu méi yǒu piányì yīdiǎn de dōngxi?
it's a gift	这是个礼物
	zhè shì gè lǐwù
please wrap it up	请把它包装起来
	qǐng bǎ tā bāozhuāng qǐlái

58

Shopping – clothes

- It is generally difficult to find larger sizes of clothes and shoes. However, in major cities like Beijing and Shanghai, there are some shops which specifically sell clothes made for the overseas markets.
- You will get designer t-shirts and jeans at very good prices if you know the art of bargaining.
- The major shopping area for designer clothes in Beijing is Xiu Shui Jie (秀水街) and in Shanghai is Xiangyang Lu (襄阳路).

may I try this on?	我可以试穿吗?
	wǒ kěyǐ shìchuān ma?
where are the changing rooms?	试衣间在哪儿?
	shìyījiān zài nǎr?
do you have a small/medium/ large size?	你们有小/中/大码吗?
	nǐmen yǒu xiǎo/zhōng/dà mǎ ma?
I'll take this one	我要买这件
	Wǒ yào mǎi zhè jiàn
I'm just looking	我先看看
	wǒ xiān kànkan
it's too expensive for me	这太贵了
	zhè tài guì le
can you give me a discount?	你可以给我打折吗?
	nǐ kěyǐ gěi wǒ dǎzhéma?
what size (clothes) do you take?	你穿多大尺寸的衣服?
	nǐ chuān duōdà chǐcùnde yīfu?
what shoe size do you take?	你穿多大尺码的鞋子?
	nǐ chuān duōdà chǐmǎde xiézi?
bigger	大些
	dàxiē
smaller	小些
	xiǎoxiē
in other colours	其它颜色
	qítā yánsè

Shopping – food

- Both the Chinese and metric system of weights and measures are widely used throughout the country. Using the Chinese weight system one 'Chinese kilogram' is almost equal to one pound.
- Outside the main cities, water should be boiled before use for either washing or drinking.
- Meat should be well cooked and served hot and vegetables should be peeled and cooked. Although in the cities there are no major problems, normal precautions should be observed when buying food from smaller restaurants or street vendors.
- In larger cities like Beijing and Shanghai, most areas have convenience stores which are open 24 hours.
- In most cities there are areas where speciality local food is sold. Authentic Chinese food is well-worth trying.
- Bottled water can be divided into two kinds, mineral and pure. Both kinds are readily available and can be found in stores, supermarkets and even street kiosks.

where can I buy...?	我在哪里可以买到…?
	wǒ zài nǎli kě yǐ mǎi dào...?
fruit	水果
	shuǐguǒ
bread	面包
	miànbāo
where is the...?	…在哪儿?
	...zài nǎr?
supermarket	超市
	chāoshì
baker's	面包店
	miànbāodiàn
butcher's	肉店
	ròudiàn

when is the market on?	市场几点开门? shìchǎng jǐdiǎn kāimén?
a litre of...	一升··· yī shēng...
milk	牛奶 niú nǎi
a bottle of...	一瓶··· yī píng...
water	水 shuǐ
wine	酒 jiǔ
beer	啤酒 pí jiǔ
a can of...	一听··· yī tīng...
coke	可乐 kě lè
a carton of...	一纸盒··· yī zhǐ hé...
juice, orange	果汁, 橙汁 guǒzhī, chéngzhī
a loaf of bread	一条面包 yī tiáo miàn bāo
250 grams of...	250克··· ér bǎi wǔ shí kè...
cheese	奶酪 nǎilào
500 grams of...	500克··· wǔ bǎi kè...
rice	大米 dàmǐ
6 eggs	六个鸡蛋 liùgè jīdàn

half a kilo of...	一斤···
	yī jīn...
fish	鱼
	yú
a tin of...	一罐···
	yī guàn...
tomatoes (tin)	西红柿罐头
	xīhóngshì guàntou
a kilo of...	一公斤···
	yī gōngjīn...
potatoes	土豆
	tǔdòu
a jar of...	一罐···
	yī guàn...
coffee (instant)	速溶咖啡
	sùróng kāfēi
a packet of...	一包···
	yī bāo...
biscuits	饼干
	bǐnggān

Daylife

Sightseeing

- Tourists will find China extremely accommodating. You can visit most of the scenic spots and places of interest every day from as early as 8am up to 6pm, with some tourist attractions staying open late into the evening.
- The best scenic places to visit in China can be found in the UN natural/cultural heritage list. It is a good idea to check the website before your trip: **http://whc.unesco.org/en/statesparties/cn**
- Travel agencies, hotels, cinemas, supermarkets, bars, pubs and restaurants are often open 24 hours a day, 7 days a week.
- Most forms of transport are available 24 hours a day, 365 days a year. However, in the first three days of the Chinese New Year most shops are closed and the frequency of transportation is greatly reduced.

where is the tourist office?	游客服务处在哪儿?
	yóukè fúwùchù zàinǎr?
where is the...?	⋯在哪儿?
	...zài nǎr?
museum	博物馆
	bówùguǎn
castle	城堡
	chéngbǎo
park	公园
	gōngyuán
temple	寺庙
	sìmiào

shrine	神殿
	shéndiàn
what can we visit in the area?	在这个地方我们可以参观什么?
	zài zhège dìfang wǒmen kěyǐ cānguān shénme?
have you any leaflets?	你们有传单吗?
	nǐmen yǒu chuándān ma?
do you have a guide in English?	你们有英语导游吗?
	nǐmen yǒu yīngyǔ dǎoyóu ma?
are there any excursions?	有没有短程旅行?
	yǒu méi yǒu duǎn chéng lǚ xíng?
is there a bus tour?	有没有观光游览车?
	yǒu méi yǒu guānguāngyóulǎnchē?
when does it leave?	什么时候出发?
	shénme shíhòu chūfā?
where does it leave from?	从哪里出发?
	cóng nǎli chūfā?
we'd like to go to...	我们想去…
	wǒmen xiǎng qù...
the monastery	修道院
	xiūdàoyuàn
is it open to the public?	它向公众开放吗?
	tā xiàng gōng zhòng kāifàng ma?
what time does it open?	几点开门?
	jǐdiǎn kāimén?
what time does it close?	几点关门?
	jǐdiǎn guānmén?
how much does it cost to get in?	门票要多少钱?
	mén piào yào duō shǎo qián?
are there reductions for children/ students/over 60s?	对儿童/学生/60岁以上的人士有优惠价吗?
	duì értóng/xuésheng/liùshísuì yǐshàngde rénshì yǒu yōuhuìjià ma?
where can I buy souvenirs?	我在哪里可以买到纪念品?
	wǒ zài nǎli kěyǐ mǎi dào jìniànpǐn?

Leisure/interests

• Cycling is extremely popular in China. Bicycle hire shops can be found everywhere, even in smaller towns. However, visitors should note that traffic and pollution levels are high, and major roads outside cities also tend to be busy.
• Downhill skiing can be practiced to the north east of China, such as in the provinces of Heilongjiang and Jilin.
• There are many fitness centres in major cities which are either independent or linked to hotels. You can enjoy a discount if you apply for a membership.
• Golf is popular in large cities like Beijing and Shanghai. There are more than 50 golf clubs in Beijing alone – most of them within one hours drive.
• There are many indoor swimming pools, outdoor tennis courts and martial arts centres.
• The Tai Chi Quan, a series of linked movements performed in a slow relaxed manner using the entire body whilst focusing the mind, is traditionally practiced in towns throughout China. This is done particularly in the early morning hours, and visitors wishing to learn or participate are welcome.

where can I/ we go...?	我/我们去哪儿可以…?
	wǒ/wǒmen qù nǎr kěyǐ...?
swimming	游泳
	yóuyǒng
fishing	钓鱼
	diàoyú
walking	步行
	bùxíng
jogging	慢跑
	mànpǎo

where can we play...?	我们在哪儿可以玩…?
	wǒmen zài nǎr kěyǐ wán...?
tennis	网球
	wǎng qiú
golf	高尔夫
	gāo ěr fū
do you have to be a member?	你必须是会员吗?
	nǐ bìxū shì huìyuán ma?
how much is it per hour?	每小时多少钱?
	měi xiǎoshí duōshǎo qián?
can we hire rackets/golf clubs?	我们可以租借球拍/高尔夫球棒吗?
	wǒmen kěyǐ zūjiè qiúpāi/gāoěrfū qiúbàng ma?
we'd like to see ... (name of team) play	我们想看 … 队的比赛
	wǒmen xiǎng kàn … duì de bǐsài
where can I/we get tickets for the game?	我/我们在哪儿能买这场比赛的票?
	wǒ/wǒmen zài nǎr néng mǎi zhèchǎng bǐsài de piào?
there are no tickets left for the game	这场比赛的票全卖完了
	zhèchǎng bǐsài de piào quán màiwán le

Walking

- Exploring the streets is a good way to get the feel of China and to get to know the cities better.
- Be careful when crossing the roads: there are pedestrian crossings and pedestrian lights, but some drivers ignore them. Keep your wits about you and use overhead walkways whenever possible.
- Hiking is also a good way to see the many natural attractions of China. There is a great variety of accessible places – mountains, waterfalls, caverns, rivers and lakes.
- A trekking permit is needed to visit some remote areas such as the Qinghai-Tibet Plateau.

• For details on individual hiking or for a list of specialised tour operators, contact the China National Tourist Office at **www.cnto.org**.

are there any guided walks?	有导游带的步行活动吗?
	yǒu dǎoyǒu dài de bùxínghuódòng ma?
do you know any good walks?	你知道有哪些好的步行活动吗?
	nǐ zhīdào yǒu nǎxiē hǎo de bùxíng huódòng ma?
how many kilometres is the walk?	这一步行活动要走多少公里?
	zhè yī bùxínghuódòng yào zǒu duōshǎo gōnglǐ?
is it very steep?	很陡峭吗?
	hěndǒuqiào ma?
how long will it take?	要花多长时间?
	yào huā duōcháng shíjiān?
is there a map of the walk?	有这一步行活动的地图吗?
	yǒu zhè yī bùxínghuódòng de dìtú ma?
we'd like to go climbing	我们想去爬山
	wǒmen xiǎng qù páshān
do you have a detailed map of the area?	你们有该地区详细的地图吗?
	nǐmen yǒu gāidìqū xiángxì de dìtú ma?

Nightlife

Nightlife – popular

• •

- Nightlife was unknown in China 20 years ago but nowadays there is a great variety of cinemas, theatres, pubs, bars, cafes, discos and Karaoke clubs. Sanlitun Bar street in Beijing is renowned for its nightlife and variety of bars with live music and shows.
- Houhai is Beijing's newly developed old town, full of small bars and pubs with character. Most of them are individually owned and have their own unique style and service.
- If you are a fan of Chinese Kong Fu, don't miss the chance to watch it live at The Red Theatre near the Temple of Heaven. The Chinese acrobatic show at the Chaoyang Theatre is also well worth a visit.
- In Shanghai, Xin Tian Di is recognized as an icon of nightlife in the city. It is a very fashionable area, with architectural styles cultivated from both the east and west. There are many international galleries, fashion shops, themed restaurants, coffee houses and bars.
- Also in Shanghai, Hengshan Road has bars in great numbers where you can take tea, coffee and many other drinks.

what is there to do in the evenings?	晚上有什么活动吗？ wǎnshàng yǒu shénme huódòng ma?
which is a good bar?	哪一间是不错的酒吧？ nǎ yījiān shì búcuò de jiǔ bā?
is it in a safe area?	周围安全吗？ zhōuwéi ānquán ma?
which is a good nightclub?	哪一间是不错的夜总会？ nǎ yījiān shì búcuò de yèzǒnghuì?

is it expensive?	消费很贵吗?
	xiāofèi hěn guì ma?
is there anything for children?	有什么孩子们可以参加的活动吗?
	yǒu shénme háizimen kěyǐ cānjiāde huódòng ma?
are there any good concerts on?	有正在上演的好音乐会吗?
	yǒu zhèngzài shàngyǎn de hǎo yīnyuè huì ma?
where can I get tickets for the concert?	我在哪儿可以购买音乐会的入场券?
	wǒ zài nǎr kěyǐ gòumǎi yīnyuèhuìde rùchǎngquàn?
where can we hear some classical music/jazz?	我们去哪儿可以听古典音乐/爵士乐?
	wǒmen qù nǎr kěyǐ tīng gǔdiǎn yīnyuè/juéshìyuè?
what's on at the cinema...(name of cinema)?	···电影院现在正在上演什么电影?
	...diànyǐngyuàn xiànzài zhèngzài shàngyǎn shénme diànyǐng?
what time does the film start?	电影什么时间开演?
	diànyǐng shénme shíjiān kāiyǎn?
how much are the tickets?	电影票多少钱?
	diànyǐngpiào duōshǎo qián?
two for the (give time of perfomance) showing	两张 ··· 开演的电影票
	liǎngzhāng ... kāiyǎn de diànyǐngpiào

Nightlife – cultural

69

• •

• There are many cultural events in major cities to attend –
concerts, Beijing opera, folk music and Chinese traditional music.
• In Beijing alone there is the National Grand Theatre, the Beijing
Concert Hall, the Imperial Garden Concert Hall and the National
Library Concert Hall.

● Traditional cultural performances such as the Beijing Opera are often shown in teahouses.

● The most famous teahouse venues are the Tianqiao Theatre and Tianqiaole Tea House, Laoshe Tea House and Liyuan Theatre where there are performances of genuine Beijing Opera and other folk music and drama every night.

● Don't worry about not understanding the language – both Chinese opera and drama make considerable use of mime and opera often has subtitle boards and is quite easy to understand.

I would like to see...	我想看···	
	wǒxiǎngkàn...	
Peking/Beijing Opera	京剧	
	jīngjù	
Shanghai Opera	越剧	
	yuèjù	
musical production	歌剧	
	gējù	
ballet	芭蕾舞	
	bāléiwǔ	
classical music concert	古典音乐会	
	gǔdiǎn yīnyuèhuì	
modern music concert	现代音乐会	
	xiàndài yīnyuèhuì	
do you have a programme of events?	你们有节目单吗?	
	nǐmen yǒu jiémùdān ma?	
what is on at the theatre?	剧院正在上演什么戏剧?	
	jùyuàn zhèngzài shàngyǎn shénme xìjù?	
what prices are the tickets?	戏票多少钱?	
	xìpiào duōshǎo qián?	
I'd like two tickets...	我想买两张票···	
	wǒ xiǎng mǎi liǎngzhāng piào...	

for tonight	今晚的
	jīnwǎn de
for tomorrow night	明晚的
	míngwǎn de
for 3rd August	八月三号的
	bāyuèsānhào de
when does the performance begin/end?	演出什么时间开始/结束?
	yǎnchū shénme shíjiān kāishǐ/jiéshù?
you can't go in, the performance has started	你不能进去, 因为演出已经开始了
	ní bùnéng jìnqù, yīnwéi yǎnchū yǐjīng kāishǐ le
you may enter at the interval	你在中间休息时可以进去
	nǐ zài zhōngjiān xiūxi shí kěyǐ jìnqù
stalls	正厅前排
	zhèngtīngqiánpái
circle	半圆形楼座
	bànyuánxínglóuzuò
box	包厢
	bāoxiāng
seat	座位
	zuòwèi
cloakroom	衣帽间
	yīmàojiān

Accommodation

Hotel (booking)

• In recent years increased tourism in China has spurred on the hotel industry. Chinese star-rated hotels meet international rankings, providing excellent service and world-class facilities.
• Many hotels are now signposted in towns. The Chinese word for a hotel is 宾馆 (bīn guǎn).
• The voltage in China is 220v, 50hz. In most bathrooms you will find an outlet for 110v but it is advisable to bring an adapter with you.
• Generally, there are two kinds of socket in China, flat blade plug and V-shaped flat prongs. If your plugs have different configurations, you will also need a plug adapter.

do you have a room for tonight?	你们这里今晚还有一间客房吗? nǐmen zhèlǐ jīnwǎn háiyǒu yījiān kèfáng ma?
I'd like to book a single room	我想预定一间单人房 wǒ xiǎng yùdìng yījiān dānrénfáng
I'd like to book a double room	我想预定一间双人房 wǒ xiǎng yùdìng yījiān shuāngrénfáng
for one night	一个晚上 yī gè wǎnshàng
... nights from ...	在 ··· 开始住 ··· 个晚上 zài ... kāishǐ zhù ... gè wǎnshàng
till...	直至··· zhízhì...
with bath	有浴缸 yǒu yùgāng

with shower	有淋浴
	yǒu línyù
with an extra bed	额外的一张小孩床
for a child	éwàide yīzhāng xiǎoháichuáng
is breakfast	早餐包括在内吗?
included?	zǎocān bāokuò zàinèi ma?
I'd like to see	我想看看房间
the room	wǒ xiǎng kànkan fángjiān
how much is it	每晚多少钱?
per night?	měi wǎn duōshǎo qián?
how much is it	每周多少钱?
per week?	měi zhōu duōshǎo qián?
have you got	你们有其它便宜一些的客房吗?
anything cheaper?	nǐmen yǒu qítā piányi yīxiēde
	kèfáng ma?

Hotel (desk)

● ●

● Usually hotels will provide boiled water in thermos bottles as tap water in China is not safe to drink.

I booked a room in	我用 … 的名字定了一间客房
the name of...	wǒ yòng … de míng zì dìng le yī jiān
	kè fáng
where can I park	我可以在哪儿停放车?
the car?	wǒ kěyǐ zài nǎr tíngfàng chē?
what time is	几点吃晚饭/早餐?
dinner/breakfast?	jǐdiǎn chī wǎnfàn/zǎocān?
the key, please	请把钥匙给我
	qǐng bǎ yàoshi gěiwǒ
please come back	请迟一点再过来
later	qǐng chíyīdiǎn zài guòlái

please clean the bathroom	请清洁浴室
	qǐng qīngjié yùshì
room number...	房间号码是···
	fángjiān hàomǎ shì...
are there any messages for me?	有给我的留言吗?
	yǒu gěiwǒ de liúyán ma?
can I send a fax?	我能发送一份传真吗?
	wǒ néng fāsòng yīfèn chuánzhēn ma?
I'm leaving tomorrow	我明天离开
	wǒ míngtiān líkāi
please prepare the bill	请准备帐单
	qǐng zhǔnbèi zhàngdān

Self-catering

• Dry cleaning and ironing shops are widely available. You can have your cleaned clothes back within 2 to 3 days.

• Cities like Beijing and Shanghai usually have self-catering apartments available for short term let. You can find out more information at **www.selfcateringchina.com** or **www.stayBeijing.com**

• Fire protection standards in Chinese accommodation may vary from what you are used to. You should check access to fire exits when you arrive.

how does the heating work?	暖气如何工作?
	nuǎnqì rúhé gōngzuò?
can you show me how this works, please?	你能向我展示如何使用这件东西吗?
	nǐ néng xiàng wǒ zhǎnshì rúhé shǐyòng zhè jiàn dōngxi ma?
whom do we contact if there are problems?	如果有问题我们联系谁?
	rúguǒ yǒu wèntí wǒmen liánxì shuí?

we need extra...	我们需要额外的…
	wǒmen xūyào éwài de...
sheets	床单
	chuáng dān
pillows	枕头
	zhěntou
is there always hot water?	一直会有热水吗?
	yī zhí huì yǒu rè shuǐ ma?
where is the nearest supermarket?	离这儿最近的超市在哪儿?
	lí zhèr zuìjìnde chāoshì zài nǎr?
where is the launderette?	哪里有自动投币的洗衣店?
	nǎli yǒu zìdòngtóubì de xǐyīdiàn?
where do we leave the rubbish?	我们把垃圾放在哪儿?
	wǒmen bǎ lājī fàng zài nǎr?

Different travellers

Children

• Hotels and restaurants in China generally don't provide childcare facilities.

• While travelling, especially in rural and remote areas, it may be difficult to feed infants. Take additional water, food and other supplies such as nappies and baby wipes that may be difficult to purchase.

• Childrens' fares are governed by height in China – those under 110cm travel free on trains, those between 110–140cm travel for half fare, over 140cm pay full fare.

a child's ticket	儿童票
	értóng piào
he/she is ... years old	他/她 ⋯ 岁了
	tā/tā ... suì le
is there a reduction for children?	儿童有优惠价吗?
	értóng yǒu yōuhuìjià ma?
do you have a children's menu?	你们有小孩子的菜单吗?
	nǐmen yǒu xiǎoháizide càidān ma?
is it OK to take children?	带孩子来行吗?
	dài háizi lái xíng ma?
what is there for children to do?	这儿有什么孩子可以玩儿的?
	zhèr yǒu shénme háizi kěyǐ wánr de?
is it safe for children?	对孩子来说安全吗?
	duì háizi lái shuō ānquán ma?
do you have a high chair?	你们有幼儿高椅子吗?
	nǐmen yǒu yòuér gāoyǐzi ma?

do you have a cot?	你们有幼儿床吗?
	nǐmen yǒu yòuérchuáng ma?
I have two children	我有两个孩子
	wǒ yǒu liǎnggè háizi
do you have any children?	你有孩子吗?
	nǐ yǒu háizi ma?

Special needs

• •

• China is trying to improve it's facilities for disabled travellers.
• Most airlines and airports now provide disabled facilities. Ask staff for assistance if you are having difficulties.
• Most modern hotels, theatres, concert hall and libraries have special services for disabled customers.

what facilities do your have for disabled people?	你们这里有哪些为残疾人士提供的设施?
	nǐmen zhèlǐ yǒu nǎxiē wèi cánjírénshì tígòngde shèshī?
are there any toilets for the disabled?	有供残疾人士使用的厕所吗?
	yǒu gòng cánjírénshì shǐyòngde cèsuǒ ma?
do you have any bedrooms on the ground floor?	你们这里一楼有卧室吗?
	nǐmen zhèlǐ yīlóu yǒu wòshì ma?
is there a lift?	有电梯吗?
	yǒu diàntī ma?
where is the lift?	电梯在哪儿?
	diàntī zài nǎr?
can you visit ... in a wheelchair?	坐轮椅的人士能去参观 … 吗?
	zuò lúnyǐde rénshì néng qù cānguān … ma?

do you have wheelchairs?	你们有轮椅吗?
	nǐmen yǒu lúnyǐ ma?
where is the wheelchair-accessible entrance?	轮椅可以进入的入口在哪儿?
	lúnyǐ kěyǐ jìnrùde rùkǒu zài nǎr?
do you have an induction loop?	你们有感应助听器吗?
	nǐmen yǒu gǎnyìngzhùtīngqì ma?
is there a reduction for disabled people?	残疾人士有优惠价吗?
	cánjírénshì yǒu yōuhuìjià ma?
is there somewhere I can sit down?	我在哪儿能坐下来?
	wǒ zài nǎr néng zuòxiàlái?

Exchange visitors (staying with you)

● There is no need to worry about cultural barriers. The Chinese are warm and friendly people and will try their best to respect and understand your customs.

what would you like for breakfast?	早餐想吃什么?
	zǎocān xiǎng chī shénme?
do you eat...?	你吃不吃…?
	nǐ chī bù chī...?
what would you like to eat?	你想吃点什么?
	nǐ xiǎng chī diǎn shénme?
what would you like to drink?	你想喝点什么?
	nǐ xiǎng hē diǎn shénme?
did you sleep well?	昨晚睡得好吗?
	zuówǎn shuì de hǎo ma?
would you like a shower?	你想洗澡吗?
	nǐ xiǎng xǐzǎo ma?

what would you like to do today?	你今天想做什么?
	nǐ jīn tiān xiǎng zuò shénme?
would you like to go shopping?	你想去购物吗?
	nǐ xiǎng qù gòuwù ma?
I will pick you up at...	我在 … 接你
	wǒ zài … jiē nǐ
did you enjoy yourself?	你玩得愉快吗?
	nǐ wán de yúkuài ma?
take care	小心一点儿
	xiǎoxīn yīdiǎnr
please be back by...	请在 … 以前回来
	qǐng zài … yǐqián huílái
we'll be in bed when you get back	你回来时我们都会睡了
	nǐ huílái shí wǒmen dōu huì shuì le

Exchange visitors (staying with them)

● You should bring a small gift when visiting a family. The Chinese love food so a food/fruit basket would be an ideal choice. Alcohol is also appreciated if you know the person enjoys it.
● During meals show your appreciation by eating well and trying a little of everything that is offered to you.
● It is etiquette at meals to finish the rice but not the dishes.
● Do not to leave your chopsticks stuck in the rice bowl when you are not using them – it is considered bad etiquette.

I like...	我喜欢…
	wǒ xǐhuān…
I don't like...	我不喜欢…
	wǒ bù xǐhuān…
that was delicious	非常美味
	fēicháng měiwèi

thank you very much	非常感谢你
	fēicháng gǎnxiè nǐ
may I phone home?	我可以给家里打电话吗？
	wǒ kěyǐ gěi jiālǐ dǎ diànhuà ma?
can I borrow...?	我能借一下 ⋯ 吗？
	wǒ néng jiè yī xià … ma?
an iron	熨斗
	yùndǒu
a hairdryer	吹风机
	chuīfēngjī
what time do you get up?	你几点起床？
	nǐ jǐdiǎn qǐchuáng?
please would you call me at...	请你在 ⋯ 点打电话给我
	qǐng nǐ zài … diǎn dǎdiànhuà gěi wǒ
can you take me by car?	你能开车载我去吗？
	nǐ néng kāichē zài wǒ qù ma?
I'm leaving in a week	我一周后离开
	wǒ yīzhōu hòu líkāi
I'm staying with...	我与 ⋯ 住在一起
	wǒ yǔ … zhù zài yīqǐ
thanks for everything	感谢你所做的一切
	gǎnxiè nǐ suǒ zuò de yīqiè
I've had a great time	我度过了非常美妙的时光
	wǒ dùguò le fēicháng měimiào de shíguāng

Difficulties

Problems

• On the whole, travel in China is safe and incident-free however major tourist sites attract thieves and pickpockets. Ensure you keep your belongings firmly with you at all times.

can you help me?	你能帮助我吗?
	nǐ néng bāngzhù wǒ ma?
I speak very little Mandarin	我只会说一点点普通话
	wǒ zhǐ huì shuō yīdiǎndian pǔtōnghuà
does anyone here speak English?	这儿有人会说英文吗?
	zhèr yǒu rén huì shuō yīngwén ma?
please speak slowly	请说慢一点儿
	qǐng shuō màn yīdiǎnr
can you show me how this works, please?	你能向我展示如何使用这件东西吗?
	nǐ néng xiàng wǒ zhǎnshì rúhé shǐyòng zhè jiàn dōngxī ma?
I would like to speak to whoever is in charge of...	我想和负责 … 的人谈谈
	wǒ xiǎng hé fùzé … de rén tántan
I'm lost	我迷路了
	wǒ mílùle
I need to get to...	我需要到 … 去
	wǒ xūyào dào … qù
how do you get to...?	去 … 怎么走?
	qù … zěnme zǒu?
I missed my train	我错过了火车
	wǒ cuòguòle huǒchē

plane	飞机
	fēijī
connection	中转
	zhōngzhuǎn
the coach has left without me	长途客车没等我上车就开走了
	chángtúkèchē méi děng wǒ shàngchē jiù kāizǒule
I've left my bag in...	我把我的包忘在了…
	wǒ bǎ wǒde bāo wàng zài le...
I have forgotten my...	我忘记带我的…
	wǒ wàng jì dài wǒ de...
I have lost my money/passport	我丢了钱/护照
	wǒ diū le qián/hùzhào
I need to get in touch with the British consulate	我需要和英国领事馆取得联系
	wǒ xū yào hé yīngguó lǐngshìguǎn qǔdé liánxì
leave me alone!	别打扰我!
	bié dǎrǎo wǒ!
go away!	走开!
	zǒukāi!

Complaints

• •

• Chinese people can be reluctant to give bad news to strangers. You'll get results more quickly if you ask questions calmly and quietly.

• Ask indirectly. For example, if a seemingly embarrassed Air China steward tells you the flight's delayed, but won't say how long, ask whether you need to book a hotel for the night, or whether it's worth going back to the city centre.

• Don't loose your temper as this will only serve to aggravate matters.

| this does not work/ it's broken | 这个不能用/坏了 |
| | zhège bùnéng yòng/huàile |

light	灯	
	dēng	
heating	暖气	
	nuǎnqì	
air conditioning	空调	
	kōngtiáo	
there is no...	没有···	
	méiyǒu...	
hot water	热水	
	rèshuǐ	
toilet paper	卫生纸	
	wèishēngzhǐ	
the room is dirty	房间很脏	
	fángjiān hěn zāng	
the bath is dirty	浴室很脏	
	yùshì hěn zāng	
it is too noisy	太吵了	
	tài chǎo le	
the room is too small	房间太小了	
	fángjiān tài xiǎo le	
this isn't what I ordered	这不是我定的东西	
	zhè búshì wǒ dìng de dōngxi	
I want to complain	我要投诉	
	wǒ yào tóusù	
there is a mistake	这是个错误	
	zhè shì gè cuòwù	
I want a refund	我要退款	
	wǒ yào tuìkuǎn	

Emergencies

● In China, the emergency numbers are: **120** for an ambulance, **119** for the fire brigade and **110** for the police.

● It is a good idea to keep a note of the phone number of your guide/tour leader, hotel or even your embassy or consulate.

● If you loose your passport, you must report it to the nearest Public Security Bureau who will issue you with a report certificate. Then contact your embassy or consulate and apply for a new passport and exit document using this certificate.

help!	救命啊!
	jiùmìng a!
fire!	着火了!
	zháohuǒle!
can you help me?	你能帮助我吗?
	nǐ néng bāngzhù wǒ ma?
there's been an accident!	出事故了!
	chūshìgùle!
someone has been injured	有人受伤了
	yǒu rén shòushāngle
someone has been knocked down	有人被撞倒了
	yǒu rén bèi zhuàngdǎole
my car crashed	我撞了车
	wǒzhuànglechē
I have crashed my car on the motorway	我在高速公路上撞了车
	wǒ zài gāosùgōnglù shang zhuàng le chē
please call the police	请叫警察
	qǐngjiào jǐngchá
please call an ambulance	请叫救护车
	qǐngjiào jiùhùchē

where is the police station?	警察局在哪儿?
	jǐngchájú zài nǎr?
I want to report a crime	我要报案
	wǒ yào bàoàn
I've been robbed/attacked	我被抢了/殴打了
	wǒbèi qiǎngle/ōudǎle
a thief has stolen my purse	小偷偷了我的钱包
	xiǎotōu tōule wǒde qiánbāo
someone's stolen my bag/traveller's cheques	有人偷了我的包/旅行支票
	yǒu rén tōule wǒ de bāo/lǚxíngzhīpiào
my car has been stolen	我的车被盗了
	wǒ de chē bèi dàole
I've been raped	我被人强奸了
	wǒ bèi rén qiángjiānle
I want to speak to a policewoman	我想和一名女警员谈话
	wǒ xiǎng hé yīmíng nǚjǐngyuán tánhuà
I need to make a telephone call	我需要打个电话
	wǒ xūyào dǎ gè diànhuà
I need a report for my insurance	我需要一份报告给保险公司
	wǒ xūyào yīfèn bàogào gěi bǎoxiǎn gōngsī
I didn't know there was a speed limit	我当时不知道有时速限制
	wǒ dāngshí bù zhīdào yǒu shísù xiànzhì
how much is the fine?	罚多少钱?
	fā duōshǎo qián?
where do I pay it?	我在哪儿付款?
	wǒ zài nǎr fùkuǎn?
do I have to pay it straightaway?	我需要马上付款吗?
	wǒ xūyào mǎshàng fùkuǎn ma?
I'm very sorry, officer	我很抱歉, 警官
	wǒ hěn bàoqiàn, jǐngguān

Health

Health

• Medical costs are surprisingly low in China but many Western medicines are not available. Bring aspirin, anti-histamines etc. with you.

• Facilities in China's international hospitals are usually as good as those in Western hospitals but it is still advisable to take out comprehensive travel insurance. The standard of medical care in remote areas, however, is not as high.

• Dial 120 for an ambulance or call your tour guide or hotel staff for help if you are unwell.

• You can also phone the SOS International, 24-hour alarm centre in Beijing or in Shanghai for advice on local medical services. Check the website: **www.internationalsos.com/en/ourresources_clinics_chinadetails.htm**

can you give me something for...?	你能给我治 … 的药吗? nǐ néng gěi wǒ zhì … de yào ma?
a headache	头疼 tóuténg
car sickness	晕车 yūnchē
a cough	咳嗽 késou
diarrhoea	拉肚子 lādùzi
is it safe for children?	孩子吃这种药安全吗? háizi chī zhèzhǒng yào ānquán ma?

how much should I give him?	我应该给他服用多少剂量?
	wǒ yīnggāi gěi tā fúyòng duōshǎo jìliàng?
I feel ill	我生病了
	wǒ shēngbìngle
I need a doctor	我需要看医生
	wǒ xūyào kàn yīshēng
my son is ill	我的儿子生病了
	wǒ de érzi shēngbìngle
my daughter is ill	我的女儿生病了
	wǒ de nǚer shēngbìngle
I'm diabetic	我患有糖尿病
	wǒ huànyǒu tángniàobìng
I'm pregnant	我怀孕了
	wǒ huáiyùnle
I'm on the pill	我一直在吃避孕药
	wǒ yīzhí zài chī bìyùnyào
I'm allergic to penicillin	我对青霉素过敏
	wǒ duì qīngméisù guòmǐn
will he/she have to go to hospital?	他/她得去医院吗?
	tā/tā děi qù yīyuàn ma?
when are visiting hours?	探病时间是什么时候?
	tànbìng shíjiān shì shénme shíhou?
I need a dentist	我需要看牙医
	wǒ xūyào kàn yáyī
I have toothache	我牙疼
	wǒ yáténg
it hurts	疼
	téng
can you give me something for the pain?	你能给我一些止疼药吗?
	nǐ néng gěi wǒ yīxiē zhǐténgyào ma?
can you do a temporary filling?	你能作临时的补牙吗?
	nǐ néng zuò línshí de bǔyá ma?

can you repair my
dentures?

你能补我的假牙吗?

nǐ néng bǔ wǒde jiǎyá ma?

will I have to pay?

我必须付钱吗?

wǒ bìxū fùqián ma?

how much will
it cost?

得要多少钱?

děi yào duōshǎo qián?

can you give me
a receipt for
the insurance?

你能给我一张保险公司要的收据吗?

nǐ néng gěi wǒ yīzhāng bǎoxiǎn
gōngsī yàode shōujù ma?

Business

Business

- In a formal situation you should always exchange business cards and shake hands with the most important person first and then work down, to avoid anyone losing face.
- Business cards should be held in both hands when they are being offered or received. When receiving another person's card, you should take the time to look at it attentively before putting it away.
- Take plenty of business cards as almost everyone you meet will want to exchange one with you.
- Business meetings always start on time and it is good practice to arrive at the meeting location early.
- The refreshment offered at meetings is usually green tea, although international offices may also offer coffee.
- You should always be smartly dressed for meetings, and when invited out for meals.

I'm...	我是…
	wǒ shì…
here's my business card	这是我的名片
	zhè shì wǒ de míngpiàn
I'm from Jones Ltd	我来自琼斯公司
	wǒ lái zì qióngsī gōngsī
I'd like to arrange a meeting with Mr/Ms...	我想安排一次与 … 先生/女士的会面
	wǒ xiǎng ānpái yīcì yǔ … xiānsheng/ nǚshì de huìmiàn
on 4 May at 11 o'clock	在5月4日11点钟
	zài wǔyuèsìrì shíyīdiǎn zhōng

can we meet at a restaurant?	我们能在饭店碰面吗?
	wǒmen néng zài fàndiàn pèngmiàn ma?
I will confirm by e-mail	我将发邮件确认
	wǒ jiāng fā yóujiàn quèrèn
what's your e-mail address?	你的邮箱地址是什么?
	nǐde yóuxiāng dìzhǐ shì shénme?
what is your website address?	你的网址是什么?
	nǐde wǎngzhǐ shì shénme?
where can I plug in my laptop?	我在哪里可以插上手提电脑的电源?
	wǒ zài nǎli kěyǐ chāshàng shǒutí diànnǎo de diànyuán?
I'm staying at Hotel...	我住在 … 宾馆
	wǒ zhùzài … bīnguǎn
how do I get to your office?	去你的办公室怎么走?
	qù nǐde bàngōngshì zěnme zǒu?
I have an appoint-ment with ... at ... o'clock	我 … 点与 … 有个约会
	wǒ … diǎn yǔ … yǒu gè yuēhuì
here is some information about my company	这是关于我公司的一些资料
	zhè shì guānyú wǒ gōngsī de yīxiē zīliào
I'm delighted to meet you	我很高兴认识你
	wǒ hěn gāoxìng rènshi nǐ
my Mandarin isn't very good	我的普通话不是很好
	wǒde pǔtōnghuà búshì hěnhǎo
I need an interpreter	我需要一个口译人员
	wǒ xūyào yīgè kǒuyì rényuán
I would like some information about the company	我想要一些关于这个公司的资料
	wǒ xiǎng yào yīxiē guānyú zhègè gōngsī de zīliào
what is the name of the managing director?	总经理叫什么名字?
	zǒngjīnglǐ jiào shénme míngzi?

Phoning – making a call

• To make a call to China dial the Chinese country code **oo 86** plus the area code without the first **o**. For Beijing **(o)10**, Guangzhou **(o)20**, Shanghai **(o)21**, then the telephone number. If you make a national call in China you dial the area code plus the number, but only the number for local calls. The full area code is always needed when using a mobile phone.

• British mobile phones work in China, but the calls are expensive so it is better to use a local provider. Buying a SIM card locally and substituting it for your regular card is an easy procedure.

• Top-up cards are widely available from convenience or grocery stores, usually advertised outside by an assortment of telephone cards hanging in a plastic wallet.

• Public phones are easy to find throughout Beijing. Most of these are now card phones and cards come in units of ¥20, ¥50 and ¥100.

where can I buy a phonecard?	我在哪儿能买一张电话卡?
	wǒ zài nǎr néng mǎi yīzhāng diànhuàkǎ?
a phonecard for ... yuan	一张 … 元的电话卡
	yīzhāng … yuán de diànhuàkǎ
I want to make a phone call	我想打个电话
	wǒ xiǎng dǎ gè diànhuà
hello	你好
	nǐhǎo
can I speak to...?	我能找 … 听电话吗?
	wǒ néng zhǎo … tīng diànhuà ma?
Mr Brun, please, extension...	我要找布伦先生, 分机号码…
	wǒ yào zhǎo bùlún xiānsheng, fēnjīhàomǎ…
is that...?	是 … 吗?
	shì … ma?

this is Mr.../Mrs...	我是 … 先生/太太
	wǒ shì … xiānsheng/tàitai
I'll call back in 5 minutes	我5分钟后打回来
	wǒ wǔ fēnzhōng hòu dǎ huílái
do you have a mobile?	你有手机吗?
	nǐ yǒu shǒujī ma?
what is your mobile number?	你的手机号码是多少?
	nǐ de shǒujī hàomǎ shì duōshǎo?
my mobile number is...	我的手机号码是…
	wǒ de shǒujī hàomǎ shì…
I will text you	我将发短信给你
	wǒ jiāng fāduǎnxìn gěinǐ
can you text me?	你能发短信给我吗?
	nǐ néng fāduǎnxìn gěiwǒ ma?
what is the code for...?	…的区号是多少?
	…de qūhào shì duōshǎo?
sorry, I must have dialled the wrong number	对不起，我拨错号码了
	duìbuqǐ, wǒ bōcuò hào mǎle
we were cut off	电话掉线了
	diànhuà diàoxiàn le
this is a very bad line	线路很不清楚
	xiànlù hěn bù qīngchu
I'll call back later	我一会再打过来
	wǒ yīhuì zài dǎguòlái
I'll call back tomorrow	我明天再打过来
	wǒ míngtiānzài dǎguòlái
how do I get an outside line?	我怎么拨打外线电话呢?
	wǒ zěnme bōdǎ wàixiàn diànhuà ne?

Phoning – answering a call

- When Chinese people make a phone call they do not normally give their own name but ask for the person they want to speak to.
- When giving telephone numbers Chinese speakers normally read out the numbers one by one. 020 7900 0283 would be read:

零二零 七九零零 零二八三

líng èr líng qī jiǔ líng líng líng èr bā sān.

who's speaking?	请问您是哪位? qǐngwèn nín shì nǎwèi?
who would you like to speak to?	请问您找哪位? qǐngwèn nín zhǎo nǎwèi?
please hold (the line)	请稍等 qǐng shāoděng
there's no reply	没人接听 méi rén jiētīng
the line is engaged	电话占线 diànhuà zhànxiàn
who shall I say is calling?	请问您是哪位? qǐngwèn nín shì nǎwèi?
I'm trying to connect you	我正在尝试为你接通电话 wǒ zhèngzài chángshì wèi nǐ jiētōng diànhuà
the line is engaged, please try later	电话正占线, 请过一会儿再打过来 diànhuà zhèng zhànxiàn, qǐng guò yīhuìr zài dǎguòlái
do you want to leave a message?	你想留言吗? nǐ xiǎng liúyán ma?
leave a message after the tone	请听到提示音后留言 qǐng tīngdào tíshìyīn hòu liúyán

Post office

• Post offices and post boxes in China are green with a green logo.
• Post boxes have their collection times marked on them.
• Domestic letters usually cost ¥ 0.60 or ¥ 0.80, while the cost of EMS (Express Mail Service) is usually more than ¥ 20.
• Postal rates for international mail vary depending on destination, weight of letter or parcel and method of delivery, so it is best to ask in the post office.

where is the post office?	邮局在哪儿?
	yóujú zài nǎr?
when does it open?	它什么时间开门?
	tā shénme shíjiān kāimén?
which is the counter...?	哪个是 … 柜台?
	nǎgè shì … guìtái?
for stamps	出售邮票
	chūshòu yóupiào
for parcels	寄包裹
	jìbāoguǒ
6 stamps for postcards...	六张寄明信片的邮票
	liùzhāng jì míngxìnpiànde yóupiào
to Britain	寄往英国
	jìwǎng yīngguó
to America	寄往美国
	jìwǎng měiguó
to Australia	寄往澳大利亚
	jìwǎng àodàlìyà
I would like to send a letter/book to the UK	我想寄封信/本书去英国
	wǒ xiǎng jì fēng xìn/běn shū qù yīngguó
how much extra does it cost to have it registered?	挂号要另付多少钱?
	guàhào yào lìngfù duōshǎo qián?

I am a stamp collector, I would like to buy the most recent stamps	我是一名集邮者，我想买最新的邮票
	wǒshì yīmíng jíyóuzhě, wǒ xiǎng mǎi zuìxīnde yóupiào
can I send this parcel to the US by sea?	我能以海运的方式将这个包裹寄往美国吗？
	wǒ néng yǐ hǎiyùnde fāngshì jiǎng zhège bāoguǒ jìwǎng měiguó ma?

E-mail/fax

- E-mail is becoming very popular in China, but it is important to check that the person you are e-mailing actually uses it. Many Chinese executives and officials have an e-mail address but do not check their mail everyday.
- Business e-mails should be brief and not too familiar or chatty.
- The code to send faxes to China from the UK is **00 86** plus the Chinese area code without the first **0**, e.g. Beijing **(0)10**, Guangzhou **(0)20**. The code to fax to the UK from China is **00 44**.
- Hotels usually charge for incoming and outgoing faxes.

I want to send an e-mail	我要发一封邮件
	wǒ yào fā yīfēng yóujiàn
what's your e-mail address?	你的邮箱地址是什么？
	nǐ de yóuxiāng dìzhǐ shì shénme?
how do you spell it?	怎样拼写？
	zěnyàng pīnxiě?
all one word	是一个字
	shì yīgè zì
all lower case (small letters)	都是小写字母
	dōushì xiǎoxiě zìmǔ
my e-mail address is...	我的邮箱地址是…
	wǒ de yóuxiāng dìzhǐ shì...

95

did you get my e-mail?	你收到我的邮件了吗?
	nǐ shōu dào wǒde yóujiàn le ma?
do you have a fax?	你有传真机吗?
	nǐ yǒu chuánzhēnjī ma?
I want to send a fax	我想发送一份传真
	wǒ xiǎng fāsòng yīfèn chuánzhēn
what is your fax number?	请问你的传真号码是多少?
	qǐng wèn nǐ de chuánzhēn hàomǎ shì duōshǎo?
my fax number is...	我的传真号码是…
	wǒ de chuánzhēn hàomǎ shì...

Internet/cybercafé

• Cybercafés are readily available in most cities. Look for the characters 网吧 (wǎngbā) on the signs on shop fronts and around the streets.

• In most of these cafés internet access can cost as little as 3 to 5 yuan an hour.

• You need to show your passport or other ID for registering as only adults are allowed to use the internet in public places as laid down by the child protection law in China.

• Most hotels provide internet service, either in the hotel-lobby (where you can expect to pay anything from 10 to 30 yuan an hour) or in your room (usually 100+ yuan for 24 hours).

• The speed of the internet is very good, though access to overseas sites is slower than in the west.

• Access to certain sites (BBC etc.) are permanently blocked.

• The cheapest way to make phone calls is by using the internet service from either **www.skype.com** or **www.internetcalls.com**.

are there any internet cafés here?	这里有网吧吗? zhèlǐ yǒu wǎngbā ma?
how much is it to log on for an hour?	上网一个小时得付多少钱? shàngwǎng yīgè xiǎoshí děi fù duōshǎo qián?
I want to check my email	我要查我的邮件 wǒ yào chá wǒde yóujiàn
how much is it for 15 minutes/for one hour?	每15分钟/一个小时多少钱? měi shíwǔ fēnzhōng/yīgè xiǎoshí duōshǎoqián?
how much is it to print something out?	打印东西多少钱? dǎyìn dōngxi duōshǎoqián?
I'd like to put these photos onto CD	我想把这些照片刻成光盘 wǒ xiǎng bǎ zhèxiē zhàopiàn kè chéng guāngpán
can you print it out?	你能把它打印出来吗? nǐ néng bǎ tā dǎyìn chūlái ma?
where can I buy a memory stick?	我在哪里可以买到记忆储存条? wǒ zài nǎli kěyǐ mǎi dào jìyìchǔ cúntiáo?
can you help me please?	请问你能帮助我吗? qǐngwèn nǐ néng bāngzhù wǒ ma?
it doesn't work	这个不能用 zhè gè bùnéng yòng
this computer has crashed	这台电脑死机了 zhè tái diànnǎo sǐjī le

Practical info

Numbers

•••

- While China uses the worldwide Arabic numeral system it also still uses its native Chinese character number system.
- The Chinese system is also a base-10 system. For zero, a simple circle is used. The difference from English, is that when you get to ten-thousand, Chinese has its own word (wàn). Chinese goes on like this until 100 million (yì), where it introduces a new character. This happens every four decimal places, unlike English where it happens every three decimal places.
- Regular Chinese characters for numbers use relatively few strokes. The characters for one, two, and three are just one, two and three parallel horizontal strokes, respectively.
- To prevent fraud when writing cheques, Chinese also uses a series of more complex characters for the numbers.
- The decimal point is expressed with the character 点 (diǎn).

0	零	líng
1	一	yī
2	二	èr
3	三	sān
4	四	sì
5	五	wǔ
6	六	liù
7	七	qī
8	八	bā
9	九	jiǔ
10	十	shí

11	十一	shíyī
12	十二	shíèr
13	十三	shísān
14	十四	shísì
15	十五	shíwǔ
16	十六	shíliù
17	十七	shíqī
18	十八	shíbā
19	十九	shíjiǔ
20	二十	èrshí
21	二十一	èrshíyī
22	二十二	èrshíèr
23	二十三	èrshísān
24	二十四	èrshísì
25	二十五	èrshíwǔ
26	二十六	èrshíliù
27	二十七	èrshíqī
28	二十八	èrshíbā
29	二十九	èrshíjiǔ
30	三十	sānshí
40	四十	sìshí
50	五十	wǔshí
60	六十	liùshí
70	七十	qīshí
80	八十	bāshí
90	九十	jiǔshí
100	一百	yībǎi
110	一百一十	yībǎiyīshí
1000	一千	yīqiān
2000	两千	liǎngqiān
million	一百万	yībǎiwàn
billion	十亿	shíyì

1st	第一	dìyī
2nd	第二	dìèr
3rd	第三	dìsān
4th	第四	dìsì
5th	第五	dìwǔ
6th	第六	dìliù
7th	第七	dìqī
8th	第八	dìbā
9th	第九	dìjiǔ
10th	第十	dìshí
15th	第十五	dìshíwǔ
20th	第二十	dìèrshí
50th	第五十	dìwǔshí
100th	第一百	dìyībǎi
101st	第一百零一	dìyībǎilíngyī
110th	第一百一十	dìyībǎiyīshí
1,000th	第一千	dìyīqiān

Fractions and percentages

½	二分之一	èr fēn zhī yī
⅓	三分之一	sān fēn zhī yī
¼	四分之一	sì fēn zhī yī
⅔	三分之二	sān fēn zhī èr
0.5	零点五	líng diǎn wǔ
3.5	三点五	sān diǎn wǔ
6.89	六点八九	liù diǎn bā jiǔ
10%	百分之十	bǎi fēn zhī shí
100%	百分之百	bǎi fēn zhī bǎi

Days and months

- In China, dates have to be written in year, month, day form.
- Months are literally, January = '1 month' 一月,
February = '2 month' 二月 and so on.

Days 日

Monday	星期一	xīngqīyī
Tuesday	星期二	xīngqīèr
Wednesday	星期三	xīngqīsān
Thursday	星期四	xīngqīsì
Friday	星期五	xīngqīwǔ
Saturday	星期六	xīngqīliù
Sunday	星期日 (天)	xīngqīrì (tiān)

Seasons 季节

spring	春天	chūntiān
summer	夏天	xiàtiān
autumn	秋天	qiūtiān
winter	冬天	dōngtiān

Months 月

January	一月	yīyuè
February	二月	èryuè
March	三月	sānyuè
April	四月	sìyuè
May	五月	wǔyuè
June	六月	liùyuè
July	七月	qīyuè
August	八月	bāyuè

September	九月	jiǔyuè
October	十月	shíyuè
November	十一月	shíyīyuè
December	十二月	shíèryuè

what is today's date?	今天是几月几日?	
	jīntiān shì jǐ yuè jǐ rì?	
what day is it today?	今天是星期几?	
	jīntiān shì xīngqī jǐ?	
5th March 2007	今天是2007年3月5日	
	jīntiān shì èrlínglíngqīnián sānyuèwǔrì	
on Saturday	在星期六	
	zāi xīngqīliù	
every Saturday	每逢星期六	
	méiféng xīngqīliù	
this Saturday	这个星期六	
	zhè gè xīngqīliù	
next Saturday	下星期六	
	xià xīngqīliù	
last Saturday	上星期六	
	shàng xīngqīliù	
in June	在六月份	
	zài liùyuèfèn	
at the beginning of June	在六月初	
	zài liùyuè chū	
at the end of June	在六月末	
	zài liùyuè mò	
before summer	夏天之前	
	xiàtiān zhīqián	
during the summer	夏季	
	xiàjì	
after summer	夏天之后	
	xiàtiān zhīhòu	
on the 20th	在20日	
	zài èrshírì	

the first of January	1月1日
	yīyuèyīrì
in 2007	在2007年
	zài èrlínglíngqīnián
in the nineteenth century	在十九世纪
	zài shíjiǔshìjì
in the Nineties	在九十年代
	zài jiǔshí niándài

Time

- China's vast territory extends across five time zones from west to east. For ease of communication Beijing Standard Time (GMT+8) is used across the country. This is 13 hours ahead of New York, eight hours ahead of UK and two hours behind Melbourne.
- Because standard time is used everywhere, travellers may find the style of living a little strange as the opening and closing times of establishments vary in keeping with normal waking hours.
- China strives to meet the needs of modern people's lives in regard to hours of operation. Post offices, museums, libraries, monuments, and even banks are open seven days a week.
- In addition to the banks being open seven days a week, one can count on most to offer 24-hour self-service.

what time is it, please?	请问现在几点了?
	qǐng wèn xiànzài jǐdiǎnle?
it's ...	现在是…
	xiànzàishì…
1 o'clock	一点钟
	yīdiǎnzhōng
2 o'clock	两点钟
	liǎngdiǎnzhōng
3 o'clock	三点钟
	sāndiǎnzhōng

6 o'clock	六点钟
	liùdiǎnzhōng
it's midday	现在是中午十二点钟
	xiànzài shì zhōngwǔ shíèrdiǎnzhōng
it's midnight	现在是半夜十二点钟
	xiànzài shì bànyè shíèrdiǎnzhōng
9	九点
	jiǔdiǎn
9.10	九点十分
	jiǔdiǎnshífēn
quarter past 9	九点一刻
	jiǔdiǎnyīkè
9.20	九点二十分
	jiǔdiǎnèrshífēn
half past 9	九点半
	jiǔdiǎnbàn
9.35	九点三十五分
	jiǔdiǎnsānshíwǔfēn
quarter to 10	差一刻十点
	chāyīkèshídiǎn
5 to 10	差五分十点
	chāwǔfēnshídiǎn

Time phrases

when does it open?	什么时间开门?
	shénme shíjiān kāimén?
when does it close?	什么时间关门?
	shénme shíjiān guānmén?
when does it begin?	什么时间开始?
	shénme shíjiān kāishǐ?
when does it finish?	什么时间结束?
	shénme shíjiān jiéshù?

at 3 o'clock	三点	
	sāndiǎn	
before 3 o'clock	三点之前	
	sāndiǎn zhīqián	
after 3 o'clock	三点之后	
	sāndiǎn zhīhòu	
today	今天	
	jīntiān	
tonight	今晚	
	jīnwǎn	
tomorrow	明天	
	míngtiān	
yesterday	昨天	
	zuótiān	
the day before yesterday	前天	
	qiántiān	
the day after tomorrow	后天	
	hòutiān	
yesterday morning	昨天上午	
	zuótiān shàng wǔ	
yesterday afternoon	下午	
	xià wǔ	
yesterday evening	晚上	
	wǎn shàng	
tomorrow morning	明天上午	
	míngtiān shàng wǔ	
tomorrow afternoon	下午	
	xià wǔ	
tomorrow evening	晚上	
	wǎn shàng	
the next day	第二天	
	dìèrtiān	

Time phrases

Holidays and festivals

Public holidays

1 January: New Year's Day   (yuándàn 元旦)
1 May: Labour Day   (wǔyīláodòngjié 五一劳动节)
1 October: National Day   (guóqìngjié 国庆节)

Chinese New Year's Day (chūnjiě 春节): This is the biggest and longest public holiday in China. It falls on a different day each year in the western solar calendar (normally the first day of the Chinese New Year ranges from the end of January to the middle of February). It always starts on the first day of each year of the Chinese lunar calendar. The celebration lasts for fifteen days.

Traditionally, families gather together, children receive money in 'red envelopes' and everyone helps make and eat a feast of jiǎozǐ 饺子; steamed dumplings with a thin skin, usually filled with pork and vegetables. Throughout this festival it is traditional to wish people wealth and happiness by saying gōngxǐ fācái 恭喜发财.

Yuánxiāojié 元宵节 Yuanxiao Festival, or Lantern Festival, is celebrated on the 15th day of the Lunar Chinese New Year. The traditional food eaten at this festival is called yuánxiāo, or tāngyuán 汤圆, a traditional sweet dumpling made of glutinous rice, with various sweet fillings.

Qīngmíngjié 清明节, sometimes translated literally as the Clear and Bright Festival, or the Tomb Sweeping festival, is celebrated on the 4th, 5th or 6th of April. It is traditionally the time when Chinese families visit graves to honour their dead ancestors and avoid eating hot food (the festival is sometimes also referred to as hánshíjié 寒食节 or Cold Food Festival).

Duānwǔjié 端午节, the Dragon Boat Festival, is celebrated on the 5th day of the 5th month of the Chinese lunar calendar. The two main activities which take place at this time are dragon boat racing and eating zòngzi 粽子; usually dates or meat covered in sticky rice and wrapped in bamboo leaves. Both of these activities originate from the festival's traditional associations with the poet and statesman Qu Yuan. According to legend, he committed suicide by jumping into the Miluo River after his loyalty to the emperor was not rewarded. The story goes that local people took to their boats and threw zòngzi into the river to feed the fish, in the hope of rescuing his body.

Guóqìngjié 国庆节 National Day, on 1 October, commemorates the anniversary of the founding of the People's Republic of China, in 1949. The PRC was declared by Chairman Mao Zedong, in Tiananmen Square in Beijing.

Zhōngqiūjié 中秋节 Mid-Autumn Festival, or moon-gazing festival, is celebrated on the 15th day of the 8th month of the Chinese lunar calendar. Traditionally families gather to observe the moon and eat yuèbǐng 月饼, mooncakes, which are round cakes made with a variety of sweet fillings including bean paste, egg and peanut. The roundness of both the full moon and the cakes symbolise the unity of the family.

The good news for visitors going to China is that most of the shops and restaurants and almost all hotels, parks and museums remain open during all the national holidays except for the first three days of the Chinese New Year. The buses, trains and planes operate during national holidays also although the frequency is greatly reduced for the first three days of the New Year celebrations.

Eating out

Chinese cuisine

Ni chī fàn le ma? is a common greeting in China and means 'have you eaten yet?' which shows us what an important part food plays in Chinese culture. To the Chinese food is life, health and good fortune. They have a wealth of cooking styles and dishes all of which make use of fresh local produce and spices. Achieving a balance in cooking is important and dishes are expected to appeal to all senses – smell, sight, taste and touch. 'Yin and Yang' (the principle of balance and harmony) should always be evident. Yin foods are generally moist and soft – fruits, vegetables etc. and have a cooling effect. Yang foods are fried and spicy with red meat and have a warming effect.

Breakfast is generally a light meal of rice porridge with deep fried dough sticks or steamed buns with various fillings washed down with hot soya milk. Lunch is eaten anytime between 11.30am and 2pm with most people using the many small street eateries to buy bowls of rice or noodles topped with vegetables and sometimes meats. Dinners are often similar to lunch unless it is a more formal family gathering, or friends are invited, in which case it can consist of several meat and vegetable dishes. Banquets, which are held on special occasions, can be amazing affairs sometimes consisting of 20 or more courses.

All major business deals and formal dinners are held at a banquet table. Dishes are served one after the other starting with cold appetisers and finishing with a thin consomme to aid digestion.

There are four main regional cuisines in China:

Northern – where a Mongolian influence is evident. It is famous for its meats, barbecued and roasted and used in Hot Pots. In this area wheat and millet are more traditionally eaten than rice. The most famous dish from this region is Peking Duck which is served with wheat pancakes, spring onions and fermented bean paste. The food from this area can sometimes be bland and basic but it is very filling.

Southern cuisine is the type of Chinese food which we are most used to in the West. Most Chinese immigrants came from the Guandong region, and rice has been grown there for nearly 2000 years. Stir frying is the most common cooking method followed by steaming. Dim Sum originated from this region. The ingredients are more varied and methods of preparation can be very sophisticated. This area does however have a reputation for the 'exotic' – lizard, rat and monkey not always being to everyone's taste!

The Eastern area has always had a fertile climate and coastline with an abundance of fish – the silver carp is a traditional delicacy. Stews where meats are simmered slowly in dark soy sauce, sugar and spices are dishes which have been made popular worldwide. Seasoning is usually light to let the natural fresh flavours be fully appreciated. Vegetarians will be at home here where the availability of ingredients has allowed Chinese vegetarian cooking to excel.

Pork, poultry, vegetables and soya are common ingredients of the Western region where red chilli, Sichuan pepper, garlic and ginger are all used to produce delicious hot spicy foods. The meat is usually marinated or pickled before frying.

Ordering drinks

- Tea is the national drink with a wide variety of quality and price.
- Coffee houses are on the increase with many western chains established.
- Soft drinks are also widely available along with bottled water.
- After tea, beer is probably the most popular drink in China with Tsingtao being the best known.
- There are many Chinese wines but the method of making these is different from in the west and some of the wines are closer to spirits. Rice wine was traditionally used in cooking rather than for drinking. Maotai is the spirit of choice for toasts at banquets.

what would you like to drink?	你想喝什么? nǐ xiǎng hē shénme?
tea, please	茶, 谢谢 chá, xièxie
with lemon	加柠檬 jiā níngméng
no sugar	不加糖 bùjiā táng
for two	要两份 yào liǎng fèn
may I have...	我能要··· wǒ néng yào...
a black coffee	一杯黑咖啡 yībēi hēi kāfēi
a white coffee	一杯加奶的咖啡 yībēi jiānǎi de kāfēi
2 white coffees	两杯加奶的咖啡 liǎngbēi jiānǎi de kāfēi
a beer	一杯啤酒 yībēi píjiǔ

large	大杯
	dà bēi
small	小杯
	xiǎo bēi
an orange juice	一杯橙汁
	yībēi chéngzhī
with ice	加冰
	jiābīng
a bottle of mineral water	一瓶矿泉水
	yīpíng kuàngquánshuǐ
sparkling	有汽泡的
	yǒu qìpàode
still	无汽泡的
	wú qìpàode
the wine list, please	请拿酒单给我
	qǐng ná jiǔdān gěi wǒ
white wine	白葡萄酒
	bái pútaojiǔ
red wine	红葡萄酒
	hóng pútaojiǔ
can you recommend a good local wine?	你能推荐当地的好葡萄酒吗？
	nǐ néng tuījiàn dāngdì de hǎo pútaojiǔ ma?
a bottle...	一瓶⋯
	yī píng...
a carafe...	一玻璃瓶的⋯
	yī bōlipíngde...

At the teahouse

● ●

● Tea houses are more expensive than Chinese coffee shops, but the cost includes a choice of tea as well as an assortment of snacks and sweets.

- The tea served varies from green tea to red tea and it is drunk more to appreciate its aroma and flavour than to quench thirst.
- Usually you sit on cushions at low tables. The tea is often brewed in a tiny teapot, and then poured into even smaller cups.

what kind of Chinese tea would you like to drink?	你想喝哪种中国茶? nǐ xiǎng hē nǎzhǒng zhōngguóchá?
I would like to drink Chinese red/ green tea	我想喝中国红/绿茶 wǒ xiǎng hē zhōngguóhóng/lǜchá
how much is a pot of tea?	请问一壶茶多少钱? qǐng wèn yīhúchá duōshǎo qián?
please add more boiled water	请再加些开水 qǐng zài jiā xiē kāishuǐ
this kind of tea is too bitter	这种茶太苦了 zhè zhǒng chá tàikǔle
this is your tip, thank you	这是给你的小费，谢谢 zhè shì gěi nǐde xiǎofèi, xièxie

Ordering food

- You will get an individual bowl, small plate and tea cup. You can hold the bowl close to your mouth and shovel in the contents with chopsticks.
- When eating from a central dish it is bad manners to touch other food or root around in the dish. If spoons or separate chopsticks are provided with the dish you should use them.
- Fill your neighbours' tea cups when they are empty and never point the spout at someone sitting around the table.
- Never wave or point with your chopsticks and certainly never leave them stuck in your rice – it resembles incense sticks in a bowl of ashes which is an omen of death.

• An important point of etiquette is that the bill should be paid by the person who made the invitation. It is polite to put up a fight but not too much of one.

I'd like to book a table for ... people	我想预定一张 ··· 人的桌子 wǒ xiǎng yùdìng yī zhāng … rénde zhuōzi
for tonight	在今晚 zài jīnwǎn
at 8 o'clock	在八点 zài bādiǎn
the menu, please	请拿菜单给我 qǐng ná càidān gěi wǒ
what is the dish of the day?	今天有什么招牌菜? jīntiān yǒu shénme zhāopáicài?
do you have a tourist menu?	你们有为游客准备的菜单吗? nǐmen yǒu wèi yóukè zhǔnbèide càidān ma?
at a set price?	价钱是固定的吗? jiàqián shì gùdìngde ma?
what is the speciality of the house?	这里的招牌菜是什么? zhèlǐde zhāopáicài shì shénme?
can you tell me what this is?	请告诉我这是什么菜? qǐng gàosù wǒ zhè shì shénme cài?
I'll have this	我要点这道菜 wǒ yào diǎn zhèdào cài
could we have a bottle of mineral water, please?	请给我们拿一瓶矿泉水好吗? qǐng gěi wǒmen ná yī píng kuàngquánshuǐ hǎoma?
excuse me!	你好! nǐhǎo!

some more bread please	请再拿一些面包来
	qǐng zài ná yī xiē miànbāo lái
some water please	请给我们拿些水来
	qǐng gěi wǒmen ná xiē shuǐ lái
the bill, please. Is the service included?	我要买单。服务费已包括在内了吗?
	wǒ yào mǎidān. fúwùfèi yǐ bāokuò zàinèi le ma?

Special requirements

●●●

• Although there are a lot of fresh vegetables used in Chinese cuisine they are often fried in animal-based oils and soups are usually made with chicken or beef stock so you will need to check.
• In larger cities vegetarianism is slowly catching on and becoming fashionable but the restaurants can often be pricey.

are there any vegetarian restaurants here?	这里有素菜饭馆吗?
	zhèlǐ yǒu sùcài fànguǎn ma?
do you have any vegetarian dishes?	你们这里有素菜吗?
	nǐmen zhèlǐyǒu sùcài ma?
which dishes have no meat?	哪些菜里没有肉?
	nǎxiē càilǐ méiyǒu ròu?
which dishes have no fish?	哪些菜里没有鱼?
	nǎxiē càilǐ méiyǒu yú?
what fish dishes do you have?	你们有哪些鱼做的菜?
	nǐmen yǒu nǎxiē yú zuò de cài?
I'm allergic to peanuts	我对花生过敏
	wǒ duì huāshēng guòmǐn
I don't like meat	我不喜欢吃肉
	wǒ bù xǐhuān chīròu
what do you recommend?	你能建议我点些什么菜吗?
	nǐ néng jiànyì wǒ diǎnxiē shénme cài ma?

Eating photoguide

Eating places

Most Chinese restaurants supply chopsticks (**Kuaì zǐ**), but knives and forks are usually available in better restaurants in larger cities. If the prices aren't displayed outside you can ask for a menu at reception. If the first price on the menu is around 10-20 RMB, then the place won't bankrupt you. Service is usually included in the bill so there is no need to tip.

Chinese Fastfood Restaurant selling popular food such as soya and dumplings (these could be described as Chinese ravioli stuffed with meat and vegetables).

115

This is a speciality restaurant serving traditional Beijing food: noodles with soybean paste. You can identify this type of restaurant by its Chinese name '老北京炸酱面'.

Chinese Tea House This is the Chinese equivalent of a pub or bar in the western world, although the atmosphere is usually much quieter. Tea is always drunk without milk or sugar.

Vinegar Instead of salt and pepper, soy sauce and vinegar stand on the table in most Chinese restaurants.

Chinese Dumplings In north China families traditionally eat dumplings when the new year is welcomed in. Dumplings are now widely available in all restaurants.

This is a very up-market Chinese restaurant which serves noble-family-style dishes. It is not overly expensive by western standards. A party of four or more people would cost roughly £30–40 each.

One of the many local restaurants you can find on the streets of China. This one specialises in spicy beef dishes.

Chinese Bakery serving traditional goods (such as mooncakes, sun cakes, and wife cakes) and western-styled goods with a Chinese influence (such as cocktail buns and egg tarts). Tea and coffee may also be served.

This restaurant specialises in Chinese-style porridge. The Chinese name is '粥'. In south China, rice with different types of meat and vegetables, is used to cook a porridge which is believed to improve your health.

This is a traditionally decorated Chinese restaurant serving snack type dishes. It will not be expensive, probably about £10 per person, depending on how many dishes you order.

Arcade where different cuisines are available.

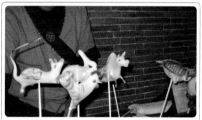

Street Vendor selling mini-sculptures made with sugar. In Chinese, it is called '糖人'.

Menu in a Chinese restaurant showing picture, name and price of the dishes available. In local restaurants not catering for the tourist trade it is quite acceptable to point out someone else's dish that you would like to order.

Restorative Food Menu Chinese food therapy (**Shí Liáo**) is a practice of healing using natural foods instead of medicine. It is particularly popular among Cantonese people who enjoy slow-cooked soups. The recipes vary infinitely, depending on the desired health benefits and taste.

Dishes

Chinese Hotpot
This is a similar idea to cheese fondue in the West. Various prepared meats and vegetables are dipped into hot soup, quickly cooked and eaten immediately.

Chinese Barbecue
In China barbecued does not mean roasted as in the West. The meat and vegetables are cooked in a hot soup as shown here.

Typical Chinese Breakfasts A cup of soya milk 豆浆 and some Chinese-styled twisted cruller 油条. Or steamed dumplings made from wheat or rice, with various stuffings.

Dishes

Typical Chinese Food Each dish is served separately to enable sharing. Shown here are fried beans with cooked seafood.

Chafing Pork flavoured with Chinese rice wine

Chinese Style Barbecue Beef, Pork And Vegetables

Stewed Pork with carved cucumber and turnip flower.

Turtle And Fish Soup

Fish In Chilli Sauce

Stewed Duck Served In Orange

Drinks

Chinese Opera This is a traditional tea house where the local opera is performing. It is common in China to combine drinking tea with some form of folk entertainment.

Traditional Tea House The girl is preparing tea. Varieties served range from green tea to black tea and it is drunk more to appreciate its aroma and flavour than to quench thirst. You usually sit on cushions at low tables.

Tea Shop Chinese tea can be classified into four main categories, green, white, black and oolong. Green is the most popular among Chinese tea drinkers.

In big cities like Beijing and Shanghai, you'll find various western style cafés selling drinks and pastries. Oriental style tea houses, however, are much more popular and serve as the social place for people to drink and chat. It is usually considered bad taste to add milk or sugar to your tea in these tea houses.

There are many Chinese wines but the method of making them differs from the west and some are closer to spirits. Rice wine was traditionally used in cooking rather than for drinking.

Chinese Liquor or **báijiǔ** is similar to Russian vodka and the most popular alcoholic drink in China. It is widely drunk at celebrations, business meetings etc. **Moutai** is one of the best known brands. **Baijiu** is generally about 40-60% proof, so it is a very potent spirit.

Beer is a popular drink in China. **Tsingtao** is one of China's top brands.

Menu reader

Soft drinks 饮料 (yǐn Liào)

七喜 qīxǐ 7up
鲜榨橙汁 xiānzhàchéngzhī fresh orange juice
绿茶 lǜchá green tea

Beers 啤酒 (pí-jiǔ)

青岛啤酒 qīngdǎo píjiǔ Qingdao beer
燕京啤酒 yànjīng píjiǔ Yanjing beer
珠江啤酒 zhūjiāng píjiǔ Zhujiang beer

Wines 酒 (jiǔ)

长城牌白葡萄酒 chángchéngpái bái pútáojiǔ Great Wall white wine
长城牌红葡萄酒 chángchéngpái hóng pútáojiǔ Great Wall red wine

Chinese rice wine

二锅头 èrguōtóu Erguotou rice wine
茅台酒 máotáijiǔ Maotai rice wine
女儿红 nǚérhóng Nerhong rice wine

Soup 汤 (tāng)

豆腐杂菜汤 dòufu zá cài tāng tofu and mixed vegetable soup
鸡蛋西红柿汤 jīdàn xīhóngshì tāng egg and tomato soup
鸡粒玉米羹 jīlì yùmǐ gēng diced chicken and sweetcorn soup
鸡肉蘑菇汤 jīròu mógu tāng chicken and mushroom soup
酸辣汤 suānlàtāng hot and sour soup
鱼片豆腐汤 yúpiàn dòufutāng sliced fish and tofu soup

Seafood 海鲜 (hǎi-xiān)

豉汁蒸鳝鱼 chǐzhī zhēng shànyú steamed eel with black bean sauce
豉汁蒸鲜鱿 chǐzhī zhēng xiānyiú steamed squid with black bean sauce
带子炒芦笋 dàizi chǎo lúsǔn stir-fried scallops with asparagus
炖鲍鱼 dùn bàoyú stewing abalone
海鲜粉丝煲 hǎixiān fěnsī bāo hot-pot of mixed seafood and vermicelli
红烧鲤鱼 hóngshāo lǐyú carp with soy sauce, ginger and Chinese wine
姜葱炒龙虾 jiāng cōng chǎo lóngxiā stir-fried lobster with ginger and spring onions
姜葱蒸带子 jiāng cōng zhēng dàizi steamed scallops with ginger and spring onions
姜葱清蒸鲢鱼 jiāng cōng qīngzhēng liányú steamed chub with ginger and spring onions
姜葱蒸鲈鱼 jiāng cōng zhēng lúyú steamed sea bass with ginger and spring onions
姜葱清蒸三文鱼 jiāng cōng qīngzhēng sānwényú steamed salmon with ginger and spring onions

女儿红酒蒸螃蟹 **nǚerhóngjiǔ zhēng pángxiè** steamed crab with Chinese rice wine

清炒大虾 **qīngchǎo dàxiā** stir-fried tiger prawns

清炒鲜鱿 **qīngchǎo xiānyóu** stir-fried squid

Chicken 鸡 (jī)

白切鸡 **báiqiējī** boiled sliced chicken

红烧鸡 **hóngshāojī** braised chicken with soy sauce and ginger

鸡块炒蘑菇 **jī kuài chǎo mógu** stir-fried diced chicken with mushrooms

鸡片炒芦笋 **jīpiàn chǎo lúsǔn** stir-fried sliced chicken with asparagus

姜葱炒鸡块 **jiāng cōng chǎo jī kuài** stir-fried diced chicken with ginger and spring onions

烤鸡 **kǎojī** roast chicken

辣子鸡丁 **làzi jīdīng** stir-fried diced chicken with chilli

栗子炖鸡 **lìzi dùn jī** braised chicken with chestnuts

腰果炒鸡丁 **yāoguǒ chǎo jīdīng** stir-fried diced chicken with cashew nuts

Beef 牛肉 (niúròu)

豉椒牛肉 **chǐjiāo niúròu** beef and green pepper with black bean sauce

红烧牛肉 **hóngshāo niúròu** braised beef with soy sauce and ginger

姜葱炒牛肉 **jiāng cōng chǎo niúròu** stir-fried beef with ginger and spring onions

牛肉炒菠萝 **niúròu chǎo bōluó** stir-fried beef with pineapple

土豆炖牛肉 **tǔdòu dùn niúròu** braised beef with potatoes

Duck 鸭 (yā)

烤鸭 **kǎo yā** roast duck
辣椒炒鸭片 **làjiāo chǎo yāpiàn** stir-fried sliced duck with chilli
酸梅汁蒸鸭块 **suānméizhī zhēng yākuài** steamed diced duck
  with plum sauce
香酥鸭 **xiāngsū yā** crispy duck

Pork 猪肉 (zhū-ròu)

叉烧（烤猪肉）**chāshāo (kǎozhūròu)** roast pork
豉汁蒸排骨 **chǐzhī zhēng páigǔ** steamed pork ribs with
  black bean sauce
咕噜肉 **gūlū ròu** sweet and sour pork
红烧肉 **hóngshāo ròu** braised pork with soy sauce and ginger
椒盐排骨 **jiāoyán páigǔ** roast pork ribs with pepper and salt
辣子肉丁 **làzi ròudīng** stir-fried diced pork with chilli
肉片炒黄瓜 **ròupiàn chǎo huángguā** stir-fried sliced pork
  with cucumber
肉片炒芦笋 **ròupiàn chǎo lúsǔn** stir-fried sliced pork with asparagus
肉丝炒青椒 **ròusī chǎo qīngjiāo** stir-fried shredded pork with
  green peppers
酸甜排骨 **suāntián páigǔ** sweet and sour pork ribs
鱼香肉丝 **yúxiāng ròusī** fish flavoured shredded pork

Lamb 羔羊 (gāoyáng)

羊肉串 **yángròuchuàn** shish kebab
炖羊肉 **dùn yángròu** braised diced lamb with soy sauce and ginger
辣羊肉丝炒胡萝卜片 **là yángròusī chǎo húluóbopiàn** stir-fried
  shredded lamb with sliced carrots and chilli

辣子炒羊肉 **làzǐ chǎo yángròu** stir-fried lamb with chilli and ginger

羊肉煲 **yángròu bāo** lamb hot-pot

Vegetables 蔬菜 (shū–cài)

蚝油炒菜心 **háoyóu chǎo càixīn** stir-fried Chinese green vegetables with oyster sauce

蚝油炒芦笋 **háoyóu chǎo lúsǔn** stir-fried asparagus with oyster sauce

凉拌海带丝 **liángbàn hǎidàisī** seaweed with soy sauce, garlic, vinegar and sesame oil

凉拌黄瓜丝 **liángbàn huángguāsī** shredded cucumber with soy sauce, garlic, vinegar and sesame oil

素炒豆芽 **sùchǎo dòuyá** stir-fried bean sprouts

蒜蓉炒大白菜 **suànróng chǎo dàbáicài** stir-fried Chinese leaf with garlic

蒜蓉炒蘑菇 **suànróng chǎo mógu** stir-fried mushrooms with garlic

蒜蓉炒青椒 **suànróng chǎo qīngjiāo** stir-fried green peppers with garlic

蒜蓉蚝油炒青菜 **suànróng háoyóu chǎo qīngcài** stir-fried Chinese vegetable with garlic and oyster sauce

鱼香茄子 **yúxiāng qiézi** fish flavoured aubergine with garlic and chilli sauce

Tofu

海鲜豆腐煲 **hǎixiān dòufu bāo** hot-pot of tofu and mixed seafood

红烧素豆腐 **hóngshāo sù dòufu** braised tofu (without meat)

肉末酿豆腐 **ròumò niáng dòufu** pork mince stuffed in tofu

虾仁酿豆腐 **xiārén niáng dòufu** prawn stuffed in tofu

Rice 大米 (dà-mǐ)

白米饭 **bái mǐfàn** boiled rice
蛋炒饭 **dàn chǎo fàn** egg fried rice

Noodles

海鲜炒面 **hǎixiān chǎo miàn** seafood chow mein
海鲜汤面 **hǎixiān tāng miàn** noodles in seafood soup
龙虾炒面 **lóngxiā chǎo miàn** lobster chow mein
什菜素汤面 **shícài sù tāng miàn** noodle in mixed vegetable soup
素炒面 **sù chǎo miàn** plain chow mein

Dumplings

素菜饺子 **sùcài jiǎozi** vegetable dumplings
鲜虾韭菜饺子 **xiānxiā jiǔcài jiǎozi** prawn and leek dumplings
羊肉饺子 **yángròu jiǎozi** lamb mince dumplings
蒸馒头 **zhēng mántou** steamed bread
猪肉大白菜饺子 **zhūròu dàbáicài jiǎozi** pork and Chinese leaf
 dumplings

Eggs 蛋 (dàn)

鸡蛋炒西红柿 **jīdàn chǎo xīhóngshì** stir-fried eggs and tomato
鸡蛋炒虾仁 **jīdàn chǎo xiārén** stir-fried eggs and prawns

Grammar

Grammatically, Mandarin is very easy and straightforward when compared with English and other European languages.

There is no change for verbs in the past tense or in the past participle and there are no irregular verbs.

The structure of a question is the same as a statement, but the extra character 吗 (ma) is added at the end.

There is no change for masculine and feminine forms of any Chinese word, unlike in French and Italian, etc. However, certain Chinese words are used only for males and certain others only for females; this is equivalent to the example of 'pretty' for females and 'handsome' for males in English.

There is also no difference between the singular and plural forms of nouns.

Nouns

A noun is a word such as 'car', 'horse' or 'Mary' which is used to refer to a person or thing.

As in English, nouns in Mandarin are unisex: you don't have to worry about which is masculine and which is feminine. In some European languages, 'apple', for instance, is feminine and 'book' is masculine.

Again, as in English, the article in Mandarin is simple:

这 (zhè) = this
那 (nà) = that.

To make things even easier, 'the' is not used in Mandarin at all!

一 (yī) in Mandarin is equal to 'a' or 'an' or 'one' in English.

However, one of the difficult areas of Mandarin is its 'measure words' for nouns. 'Measure words' don't exist in English. For example, in English you say 'one horse'. In Mandarin you say 'one' + the measure word for 'horse' + 'horse': 一匹马 (yīpǐ mǎ). There are quite a few different measure words for different nouns.

个 (gè) is used most frequently. It can be used for people and objects i.e. most nouns. The good news for anybody who is talking to Chinese people in basic Mandarin is that you should simply use this measure word for all the nouns if you don't know which measure word is the right one. Chinese people will still understand you.

Other commonly used measure words:

本	(běn)	for book, dictionary and magazine, etc.
辆	(liàng)	for car, bus and train
架	(jià)	for plane
匹	(pǐ)	for horse
头	(tóu)	for pig, cow, sheep
尾	(wěi)	for fish
艘	(sōu)	for boat
只	(zhī)	for chicken, duck, goose

Pronouns

A pronoun is a word that you use to refer to someone or something when you do not need to use a noun, often because the person or thing has been mentioned earlier. Examples are 'it', 'she/he', 'something' and 'myself'.

They are easier in Mandarin than in English; all pronouns in Mandarin stay the same whether they are used as subjects or objects.

Subject	Object	Mandarin pronouns
I	me	我 (wǒ)
you (singular)	you	你 (nǐ)
you (plural)	you	你们 (nǐmen)
he	him	他 (tā)
she	her	她 (tā)
it	it	它 (tā)
we	us	我们 (wǒmen)
they	them	他/她们 (tāmen)
things	them	它们 (tāmen)

Adjectives

An adjective is a word such as 'small', 'pretty' or 'practical' that describes a person or thing, or gives extra information about them.

In Mandarin, adjectives are either in front of or after the noun they describe, e.g.

the red apple	红苹果
	hóng píngguǒ
the apple is red	苹果是红的
	píngguǒ shì hóngde

Please note that 是 (shì) 'to be' and 的 (de) go before and after the adjective in the second example.

In Mandarin some adjectives are used only to describe men and some are used only to describe women, e.g.

handsome young man	英俊的小伙子
	yīngjùnde xiǎo huǒzi
pretty girl	漂亮的姑娘
	piàoliàngde gūniang

My, your, his, her, our, their

In Mandarin, you simply add 的 (de) at the end of the above pronouns to make them become adjectives:

my	我的 (wǒde)
your (singular)	你的 (nǐde)
you (plural)	你们的 (nǐmende)
his	他的 (tāde)
her	她的 (tāde)
its	它的 (tāde)
our	我们的 (wǒmende)
their	他/她们的 (tāmende)
things	它们的 (tāmende)

Verbs

A verb is a word such as 'sing', 'walk' or 'cry' which is used with a subject to say what someone or something does or what happens to them.

In Mandarin, verbs are not divided into regular and irregular, making it easy for beginners to try to build a simple sentence; e.g.

| I like you | 我喜欢你 |
| | **wǒ xǐhuan nǐ** |

In Mandarin verbs do not have to change when used in the past tense or as present participles or past participles. Terms such as 'yesterday' and 'in the past' used before the verb are sufficient to indicate that something happened or has happened. Please note you normally add 了 (**le**) after the verb when this verb is being used in the past tense; e.g.

| I went to London yesterday | 我昨天去了伦敦 |
| | **wǒ zuótiān qùle lúndūn** |

In Mandarin you say 'I yesterday go to London'. When using a verb as a present or past participle, you normally add 过 (**guò**) after the verb; e.g.

| I have/had been to London | 我去过伦敦 |
| | **wǒ qùguò lúndūn** |

List of commonly used verbs:

吃 (chī)   eat
买 (mǎi)   buy
卖 (mài)   sell
爱 (ài)   love
去 (qù)   go
喜欢 (xǐhuan)   like

To make a verb negative in Mandarin, you simply insert 不 (bù)
before the verb, e.g.

I am not eating   我不吃
                      wǒ bùchī

Building basic sentences

As in English, in Chinese there are only a few different structures
for basic sentences, as follows:

I am Chinese	我是中国人
	wǒ shì zhōngguórén
I like/fancy you	我喜欢你
	wǒ xǐhuan nǐ
do you like/ fancy me?	你喜欢我吗?
	nǐ xǐhuan wǒ ma?
I have been to Beijing	我去过北京
	wǒ qùguò Běijīng

Dictionary

A

A & E 急诊室 jízhěnshì

about 关于 guānyú

a book about London
关于伦敦的一本书 guānyú Lúndūn de yīběn shū

a(n) 一 yī

able 能够 néng gòu

above 在 ⋯ 上面 zài ... shàngmiàn

abroad: *to go abroad* 到国外 dào guó wài

abscess 脓肿 nóngzhǒng

accelerator 加速器 jiāsùqì

accent 口音 kǒuyīn

to accept 接受 jiēshòu

accident 事故/意外 shìgù/yìwài

accident & emergency department 急诊室 jízhěnshì

accommodation 住处 zhùchù

account (with bank, at shop) 账户 zhànghù

accountant 会计师 kuàijìshī

ache 痛 tòng

I've got (a) stomach/toothache
我胃/牙痛 wǒ wèi/yá tòng

across 穿过 chuānguò

actor 演员 yǎnyuán

actress 女演员 nǚ yǎnyuán

adapt 使适合 shǐ shìhé

adaptor 转接器 zhuǎnjiēqì

addition 加法 jiāfǎ

address 地址 dìzhǐ

address book 通讯录 tōngxùnlù

adhesive tape 胶带 jiāodài

adjustable 可调节的 kě tiáojié de

administrator 管理人员 guǎnlǐ rényuán

admire 佩服 pèifú

admission 进入许可 jìnrù xǔkě

adopt (approach, attitude, plan) 采用 cǎiyòng

(child) 收养 shōuyǎng

adult 成年人 chéng nián rén

advance: *in advance* 提前 tí qiǎn

adventure 冒险活动 màoxiǎn huódòng

advertisement 广告 guǎnggào

advice 忠告 zhōnggào

aeroplane 飞机 fēijī

aerosol 按钮式喷雾器 ànniǔshì pēnwùqì

afternoon 下午 xiàwǔ

afford 买/支付得起某物 mǎi/zhīfùdeqǐ mǒuwù

afraid 害怕 hàipà

to be afraid 害怕某人/某物 hàipà mǒurén/mǒuwù

after 在 ⋯ 以后 zài ... yǐhòu

afterwards 以后 yǐhòu

again 又一次地 yòu yīcì de

against 紧靠在 jǐnkào zài

age 年龄 niánlíng

age limit 年龄限制 niánlíng xiànzhì

agency 代理处 dàilìchù

ago: *2 days ago* 两天前 liǎngtiān qián

long ago/a long time ago
很久以前 hěnjiǔ yǐqián

agree 同意 tóngyì

agreement: *an agreement*
(关于某事的)协议 (guānyú mǒushì de) xiéyì

agriculture 农业 nóngyè

ahead 在前地 zàiqián de

AIDS 艾滋病 àizībìng

aim: *to aim*
将某物瞄准(某人/某物) jiāng mǒuwù miáozhǔn (mǒurén/mǒuwù)

air 空气 kōngqì

airbag 安全气袋 ānquán qìdài

airbed 充气床垫 chōngqì chuángdiàn

air conditioning 空调 kōngtiáo

air hostess 空中小姐 kōngzhōng xiǎojiě

airline 航空公司 hángkōng gōngsī

airmail: by airmail 航空邮寄 hángkōng yóujì

airport 机场 jīchǎng

airtight 密封的 mìfēng de

aisle 过道 guòdào

à la carte 照菜单点 zhào càidān diǎn

alarm 警报器 jǐngbàoqì

alarm call 唤醒电话 huànxǐng diànhuà

alarm clock 闹钟 nàozhōng

alcohol 酒 jiǔ

alcohol-free (beer, wine) 无酒精的 wú jiǔjīng de

all 所有的 suǒyǒu de

all day/night 整日/夜 zhěngrì/yè

allergic to 对 … 过敏 duì … guòmǐn

to allow 允许 yǔnxǔ

all right: to be all right 还不错的 hái bùcuò de

almond 杏仁 xìngrén

almost 差不多 chàbùduō

I spent almost a month in China 我在中国呆了差不多一个月 wǒ zài Zhōngguó dāile chàbùduō yīgè yuè

alone 独自的 dúzì de

along 沿着 yánzhe

alphabet 字母表 zìmǔbiǎo

already 已经 yǐjīng

also 也 yě

alter 更改 gēnggǎi

always 总是 zǒngshì

a.m. 上午 shàngwǔ

amber 琥珀色的 hǔpòsè de

ambulance 救护车 jiùhùchē

America 美洲 Měizhōu

American 美国的 Měiguó de
(person) 美国人 Měiguórén

among(st) 在 … 当中 zài … dāngzhōng

amount 数量 shùliàng

amuse 使发笑 shǐ fāxiào

amusement 愉悦 yúyuè

amusement park 游乐场 yóulèchǎng

anaemia 贫血症 pínxuèzhèng

anaesthetic 麻醉剂 mázuìjì

general anaesthetic 全身麻醉 quánshēn mázuì

local anaesthetic 局部麻醉 júbù mázuì

under anaesthetic 处于麻醉状态 chǔyú mázuì zhuàngtài

ancestor 祖先 zǔxiān

anchor 锚 máo

ancient 古代的 gǔdài de

and 和 hé

angel 天使 tiānshǐ

angina 心绞痛 xīnjiǎotòng

angry 生气的 shēngqì de

animal 动物 dòngwù

ankle 踝 huái

anniversary (某事的)周年纪念 (mǒushì de) zhōunián jìniàn

announce 宣布 xuānbù

announcement 宣布 xuānbù

annoying 讨厌的 tǎoyàn de

annual (meeting, report) 每年的 měinián de

anorak 连帽防风夹克 liánmào fángfēng jiākè

another 另外的 lìngwàide

answer 回答 huídá

answering machine 电话答录机 diànhuà dálùjī

ant 蚂蚁 mǎyǐ

anthem 赞美诗 zànměishī

antibiotic 抗生素 kàngshēngsù
anti-depressant 抗抑郁症药 kàng yìyùzhèng yào
antidote 解毒剂 jiědújì
antifreeze 防冻剂 fángdòngjì
antique 古董 gǔdǒng
antiseptic 杀菌剂 shājūnjì
antisocial 有碍社会的 yǒu ài shè huì de
anxious 担心的 dān xīn de
any 一些的 yīxiē de
have you got any chocolate/sweets?
你有巧克力/糖吗? nǐ yǒu qiǎokèlì/táng ma?
I haven't any chocolate/sweets
我没有巧克力/糖 wǒ méiyǒu qiǎokèlì/táng?
anyone 任何人 rènhé rén
anything 任何事 rènhé shì
anytime 任何时候 rènhé shíhou
anywhere 任何地方 rènhé dìfang
apartment 公寓 gōngyù
aperitif 开胃酒 kāiwèijiǔ
apologize 道歉 dàoqiàn
appendicitis 阑尾炎 lánwěiyán
appetizer 开胃食品 kāiwèi shípǐn
apple 苹果 píngguǒ
application form 申请表格 shēnqǐng biǎogé
appointment 约会 yuēhuì
approval 批准 pīzhǔn
approximately 大约地 dàyuē de
apricots 杏子 xìngzi
April 四月 sìyuè
architect 建筑师 jiànzhùshī
area 地区 dìqū
argument 争吵 zhēngchǎo
arm 臂 bì
aromatherapy 芳香疗法 fāngxiāng liáofǎ
around 到处 dàochù
arrange 安排 ānpái
arrangement 约定 yuēdìng
arrest 逮捕 dàibǔ

arrivals (plane, train) 抵达 dǐdá
arrive 到 dào
art 艺术 yìshù
art gallery 美术馆 měishùguǎn
arthritis 关节炎 guānjiéyán
artificial 人造的 rénzào de
artist 艺术家 yì shù jiā
ashore 在岸上 zài àn shàng
ashtray 烟灰缸 yānhuīgāng
ask: *to ask a question*
问(某人)一个问题 wèn (mǒurén) yígè wèntí
asking price 索价 suǒjià
asleep 睡着的 shuìzháo de
to be asleep 睡着了 shuìzháo le
asparagus 芦笋 lúsǔn
aspirin 阿司匹林 āsīpǐlín
assault 攻击 gōngjī
assistance 帮助 bāngzhù
asthma 哮喘病 xiàochuǎn bìng
at 在 zài
at four o'clock 在4点钟 zài sìdiǎn zhōng
at home 在家 zàijiā
at night 在晚上 zài wǎnshàng
athlete 运动员 yùndòngyuán
athletics 田径运动 tiánjìng yùndòng
the Atlantic (Ocean) 大西洋 Dàxīyáng
atlas 地图册 dìtúcè
ATM (Automated Telling Machine) 自动取款机 zìdòng qǔkuǎnjī
attach 附上 fùshàng
attachment (computer file, of tool) 附件 fùjiàn
attack 袭击 xíjī
attend (conference, lecture) 参加 cān jiā
attendant 服务员 fúwùyuán
attic 阁楼 gélóu
attractive 有魅力的 yǒu mèilì de
aubergine 茄子 qiézi
auction 拍卖 pāimài

audience 观众 guānzhòng
August 八月 bāyuè
Australia 澳大利亚 Àodàlìyà
Australian 澳大利亚的 Àodàlìyà
de
(person) 澳大利亚人 Àodàlìyàrén
authentic 正宗的 zhèngzōng de
author 作家 zuòjiā
automatic car 自动挡
zìdòngdǎng
autumn 秋天 qiūtiān
available 可用的 kě yòng de
avalanche 雪崩 xuěbēng
avenue 大街 dàjiē
average 平均的 píngjūn de
avoid 避免 bìmiǎn
awake: to be awake 醒着的
xǐngzhe de
away …开 …kāi
awful 糟糕的 zāogāo de
axle 轴 zhóu

B

baby 婴儿/宝宝 yīng'ér/bǎobao
baby food 婴儿食品 yīng'ér shípǐn
babysitter 保姆 bǎomǔ
bachelor 单身汉 dānshēnhàn
back 背部 bèibù
backache 背痛 bèitòng
backpack 背包 bēibāo
backup (copy, disk, file) 备份的
bèifèn de
bacon 腌猪肉 yān zhūròu
bad 坏 huài
(fruit, meat etc) 腐烂的 fǔlàn de
badminton 羽毛球 yǔmáoqiú
bag 包 bāo
(handbag) 手袋 shǒudài
(suitcase) 行李箱 xínglixiāng
baggage 行李 xíngli
baggage allowance 行李限重
xíngli xiànzhòng
baggage reclaim 领取行李
lǐngqǔxíngli

bait 鱼饵 yú'ěr
bake 烤 kǎo
baked potato 烤土豆 kǎo tǔdòu
baker's 面包店 miànbāodiàn
balcony 露台 lùtái
bald 秃的 tū de
(tyre) 严重磨损的 yánzhòng mósǔn
de
ball 球 qiú
ballet 芭蕾舞 bālěiwǔ
balloon (child's) 气球 qìqiú
(hot-air balloon) 热气球 rèqìqiú
ballpoint (pen) 圆珠笔 yuánzhūbǐ
bamboo 竹子 zhúzi
bamboo shoots 竹笋 zhúsǔn
banana 香蕉 xiāngjiāo
band (jazz, rock etc) 乐队 yuèduì
bandage 绷带 bēngdài
bank 银行 yínháng
bank account 银行账户 yínháng
zhànghù
bank card 银行卡 yínhángkǎ
banknote 纸币 zhǐbì
bankrupt 破产的 pòchǎn de
banquet 盛宴 shèngyàn
bar 酒吧 jiǔbā
bar (chocolate, of soap) 块 kuài
barbecue 烤肉 kǎoròu
barber shop 理发店 lǐfà diàn
bargain 廉价品 liánjiàpǐn
bark (of dog) 犬吠声 quǎnfèishēng
(of tree) 树皮 shùpí
barley 大麦 dàmài
barn 仓房 cāngfáng
barrel 桶 tǒng
barrier (at frontier, entrance) 阻拦
zǔlán
basement 地下室 dìxiàshì
basin 盆 pén
basket 筐 kuāng
basketball 篮球 lánqiú
bat 蝙蝠 biānfú
(for table tennis) 球拍 qiúpāi
bathtub 浴缸 yùgāng

to take a bath 洗澡 xǐzǎo
bathrobe 浴衣 yùyī
bathroom 浴室 yùshì
bath towel 浴巾 yùjīn
battery (radio etc) 电池 diànchí
bay 湾 wān
(for loading, parking etc) 隔间 géjiàn
beach 沙滩 shātān
bean 豆 dòu
coffee/cocoa beans 咖啡/可可豆 kāfēi/kěkě dòu
bean sprouts 豆芽 dòuyá
bear 熊 xióng
beard 胡须 húxū
beautiful 美丽的 měilìde
beauty parlour 美容院 měiróngyuàn
because 因为 yīnwéi
become 成为 chéngwéi
bed 床 chuáng
(double) 双人床 shuāngrénchuáng
(single) 单人床 dānrénchuáng
bed and breakfast 住宿加早餐 zhùsù jiā zǎocān
bedding 床上用品 chuángshang yòngpǐn
bedroom 卧室 wòshì
bee 蜜蜂 mìfēng
beef 牛肉 niúròu
roast beef 烤牛肉 kǎo niúròu
beefburger 牛肉汉堡包 niúròu hànbǎobāo
beer 啤酒 píjiǔ
before 之前 zhīqián
beggar 乞丐 qǐgài
begin 开始 kāishǐ
behind 在 … 后面 zài … hòumian
Beijing 北京 Běijīng
believe 相信 xiāngxìn
bell (of church) 钟 zhōng
(on door) 门铃 ménlíng
belong 属于 shǔyú
below 在 … 之下 zài … zhīxià
belt 腰带 yāodài

bench 长椅 chángyǐ
bend 弯 wān
beneath 在 … 之下 zài … zhīxià
berry 浆果 jiāngguǒ
berth 卧铺 wòpù
beside 在 … 旁边 zài … pángbiān
best 最好的 zuìhǎo de
best-before date 保质期 bǎozhì qī
bet 赌注 dǔzhù
to bet on 下赌注于 xià dǔzhù yú
better 更好的 gènghǎo de
between 在 … 中间 zài … zhōngjiān
beware! 注意! zhùyì!
beyond 在 … 的另一边 zài … de lìng yībiān
bib 围嘴 wéizuǐ
bicycle 自行车 zìxíngchē
bicycle pump 自行车打气筒 zìxíngchē dǎqìtǒng
big 大 dà
bigger 大些 dàxiē
bikini 比基尼 bǐjīní
bill (hotel, restaurant) 帐单 zhàngdān
billion 十亿 shíyì
bin 垃圾箱 lājīxiāng
binoculars 双筒望远镜 shuāngtǒng wàngyuǎnjìng
bird 鸟 niǎo
Biro 圆珠笔 yuánzhūbǐ
birth 出生 chūshēng
birth certificate 出生证明 chūshēng zhèngmíng
birth control 节育 jiéyù
birthday 生日 shēngrì
happy birthday! 生日快乐! shēngrìkuàilè!
my birthday is on… 我的生日是… wǒ de shēngrì shì…
birthday card 生日贺卡 shēngrì hèkǎ
birthday present 生日礼物 shēngrì lǐwù
biscuits 饼干 bǐnggān

a bit 一点 yīdiǎn

bite 咬 yǎo

bitter (taste) 苦 kǔ

black 黑色 hēisè

blackberry 黑莓 hēiméi

blame 责备 zébèi

blank 空白的 kòngbái de

blanket 毛毯 máotǎn

bleach 去污液 qùwūyè

bleed 流血 liúxuè

blend 混合物 hùnhéwù

blender 搅拌器 jiǎobànqì

block 街区 jiēqū

blockage 堵塞 dǔsè

blond(e) (hair) 金色的 jīnsè de

blonde (person) 金发的人 jīnfà de rén

blood 血 xuè

blood group 血型 xuèxíng

blood pressure 血压 xuèyā

high/low blood pressure 高/低血压 gāo/dīxuèyā

blood test 验血 yànxuè

blouse 女衬衫 nǚ chènshān

blow-dry 吹干 chuīgān

blue (light) 蓝色的 lánsè de

blunt 钝的 dùn de

boarding gate 登机口 dēngjīkǒu

boat 船 chuán

body 身体 shēntǐ

boil 烧开 shāokāi

boiler 锅炉 guōlú

bomb 炸弹 zhàdàn

bone 骨头 gǔtou

bone (fish, meat) 剔除骨刺 tīchú gǔcì

bonfire 篝火 gōuhuǒ

bonnet (of car) 发动机罩盖 fādòngjīzhàogài

book 书 shū

book (of stamps, tickets) 册 cè

to book; booking 预订 yùdìng

booking office 售票处 shòupiàochù

bookshop 书店 shūdiàn

boot 靴子 xuēzi

(of car) 车后行李箱 chē hòu xínglixiāng

boots (ankle) 短靴子 duǎn xuēzi

(long) 长靴子 cháng xuēzi

border 边界 biānjiè

boring 乏味的 fáwèi de

borrow 借 jiè

can I borrow a pen please? 我能不能借支笔? wǒ néngbùnéng jiè zhī bǐ?

boss 老板 lǎobǎn

both 两者都 liǎngzhě dōu

bottle 瓶 píng

bottle of wine 一瓶酒 yī píng jiǔ

bottle opener 开瓶器 kāipíngqì

bottom 底部 dǐbù

boutique 小型精品店 xiǎoxíng jīngpǐndiàn

bowl 碗 wǎn

bow tie 领结 lǐngjié

box 盒子 hézi

(theatre) 包厢 bāoxiāng

boxer shorts 平角裤 píngjiǎokù

boxing 拳击 quánjí

box office 售票处 shòupiàochù

boy (young child) 男孩 nánhái

boyfriend 男朋友 nánpéngyou

bra 文胸 wén xiōng

bracelet 手镯 shǒuzhuó

brain 脑 nǎo

brake 刹 shā

brake light 刹车灯 shāchēdēng

brakes 刹车闸 shāchēzhá

branch 树枝 shùzhī

(of shop) 分店 fēndiàn

brand (make) 品牌 pǐnpái

brand-new 全新的 quánxīn de

brandy 白兰地 báilándì

bread 面包 miànbāo

breadbin 面包箱 miànbāoxiāng

breadcrumbs 面包屑 miànbāoxiè

break 打碎 dǎsuì

(arm, leg) 弄断 nòngduàn
breakdown 故障 gùzhàng
breakfast 早餐 zǎocān
break-in 闯入 chuǎngrù
breast (of chicken, lamb) 胸脯肉 xiōngpúròu
breast-feed 母乳哺养 mǔrǔ bǔyǎng
breathe 呼吸 hūxī
breathing difficulties 呼吸困难 hūxīkùnnán
breath test 酒精呼吸分析 jiǔjīng hū xī fēnxī
breezy 惠风和畅的 huìfēng héchàng de
brick 砖 zhuān
bride 新娘 xīnniáng
bridegroom 新郎 xīnláng
bridesmaid 伴娘 bànniáng
bestman 伴郎 bànláng
bridge 桥 qiáo
briefcase 手提箱 shǒutíxiāng
bright 亮的 liàng de
Britain 英国 yīngguó
British 英国的 yīngguóde
broad 宽的 kuān de
broadband 宽带 kuāndài
broad bean 蚕豆 cándòu
broadcast 广播 guǎngbō
broccoli 花椰菜 huāyēcài
brochure 小册子 xiǎocèzi
broken 破碎的 pòsuì de
bronchitis 支气管炎 zhīqìguǎnyán
bronze 青铜 qīngtóng
brooch 胸针 xiōngzhēn
broom 扫帚 sàozhou
brother 兄弟 xiōngdì
brown 棕色 zōngsè
browse (on the internet) 浏览 liúlǎn
browser 浏览器 liúlǎnqì
bruise 青瘀 qīngyū
brush (for cleaning, for decorating) 刷子 shuāzi
(for hair) 发刷 fàshuā

bubble bath 泡泡浴液 pàopào yùyè
bucket 桶 tǒng
buckle 扣环 kòuhuán
buffet car 餐车 cānchē
buggy (for baby) 婴儿车 yīng'érchē
build 建造 jiànzào
building 建筑物 jiànzhùwù
building site 建筑工地 jiànzhù gōngdì
bulb 电灯泡 diàndēngpào
bull 公牛 gōngniú
bumper 保险杠 bǎoxiǎngàng
bunch (of bananas, grapes, keys) 串 chuàn
(of flowers) 束 shù
bungee jumping 蹦极跳 bèngjítiào
bunk beds 双层床 shuāngcéngchuáng
bureau (for information, travel etc) 办事处 bànshìchù
bureau de change 兑换处 duìhuànchù
burger 汉堡包 hànbǎobāo
burglar 盗窃犯 dàoqièfàn
burglar alarm 防盗铃 fángdàolíng
burglary 盗窃 dàoqiè
burn 烧焋 shāo hú de
sunburn 晒伤 shàishāng
burning 着火的 zháohuǒ de
burst 爆裂 bàoliè
bus 公共汽车 gōnggòngqìchē
bus driver 公共汽车司机 gōnggòng qìchē sījī
bus pass 公交车通票 gōngjiāochē tōngpiào
bus shelter 公交车候车亭 gōngjiāochē hòuchētíng
bus station 公共汽车站 gōnggòngqìchēzhàn
bus stop 公共汽车站 gōnggòngqìchēzhàn
bus ticket 公共汽车车票 gōnggòngqìchē chēpiào
business 商务 shāngwù

businessman 商人 shāngrén
business trip 出差 chūchāi
businesswoman 女商人 nǚ shāngrén
busy (person) 忙的 máng de
(day, schedule, time) 忙碌的 mánglù de
(shop, street) 繁忙的 fánmáng de
but 但是 dànshì
butcher's 肉店 ròudiàn
butter 黄油 huángyóu
butterfly 蝴蝶 húdié
button 钮扣 niǔkòu
buy 买 mǎi
by (next to) 邻近 línjìn
by bus 乘坐公共汽车 chéngzuò gōnggòngqìchē
by car 坐轿车 zuò jiàochē
by train 坐火车 zuò huǒchē
bypass 旁道 pángdào
byte 字节 zìjié

C

cab (taxi) 出租车 chūzūchē
cabaret 餐馆夜总会里的歌舞表演 cānguǎn yèzǒnghuìlǐ de gēwǔ biǎoyǎn
cabbage 卷心菜 juǎnxīncài
cabin 舱 cāng
cabin crew 机组人员 jīzǔ rényuán
cabinet 贮藏橱 zhùcáng chú
cable car 缆车 lǎnchē
cable television 有线电视 yǒuxiàn diànshì
café 咖啡吧 kāfēibā
cake 蛋糕 dàngāo
cake shop 蛋糕店 dàngāodiàn
calculator 计算器 jìsuànqì
calendar 日历 rìlì
call 把 … 叫作 bǎ … jiào zuò
(phonecall) 打(电话) dǎ (diànhuà)
calligraphy 书法 shūfǎ
calm (sea) 平静的 píngjìng de
Calor gas 罐装煤气 guànzhuāng méiqì

camcorder 录象机 lùxiàngjī
camera 相机 xiàngjī
camp: *to go camping* 外出露营 wàichū lùyíng
campsite 野营地 yěyíngdì
can 罐头 guàntou
can (to be able) 可以/能 kěyǐ/néng
can I...? 我可以/能 … 吗? wǒ kěyǐ/néng … ma?
can I help you? 您要买点儿什么? nín yào mǎidiǎn shénme?
can we...? 我们可以/能 … 吗? wǒmen kěyǐ/néng … ma?
Canada 加拿大 Jiānádá
Canadian 加拿大的 Jiānádá de
(person) 加拿大人 Jiānádàrén
canal 运河 yùnhé
cancel 取消 qǔxiāo
cancer 癌症 áizhèng
candle 蜡烛 làzhú
canned 罐装的 guànzhuāng de
canoe 独木船 dúmùchuán
can opener 开罐器 kāi guànqì
Cantonese 广东的 Guǎngdōng de
(language) 广东话 Guǎngdōnghuà
(person) 广东人 Guǎngdōngrén
cap 帽 mào
capital (city) 首都 shǒudū
(letter) 大写字母 dàxiě zìmǔ
car 轿车 jiàochē
carafe 精美的盛葡萄酒或水的玻璃容器 jīngměi de chéng pútáo jiǔ huò shuǐ de bōlí róngqì
caravan 活动住房 huódòng zhùfáng
caravan site 活动住房停放处 huódòng zhùfáng tíngfàngchù
carburettor 汽化器 qìhuàqì
card (bank card, credit card) 信用卡 xìnyòngkǎ
(business card) 名片 míngpiàn
(greetings card) 贺卡 hèkǎ
(playing card) 扑克牌 pūkèpái

cardigan 开襟毛衣 kāijīn máoyī

careful 小心的 xiǎoxīn de

to be careful (not) to do something
小心(别)做某事 xiǎoxīn (bié) zuò mǒushì

car ferry 汽车渡轮 qìchē dùlún

car hire 汽车出租 qìchē chūzū

car keys 车钥匙 chē yàoshi

car park 停车场 tíngchēchǎng

carpet 地毯 dìtǎn

car rental 汽车出租 qìchē chūzū

carriage 车厢 chēxiāng

carrots 胡萝卜 húluóbo

carry 抱 bào

carton 纸箱 zhǐxiāng

cartoons 卡通片 kǎtōngpiàn

carve 把 ··· 切片 bǎ ... qiēpiàn

carving 雕刻品 diāokèpǐn

car wash 汽车擦洗 qìchē cāxǐ

case 行李箱 xínglixiāng

cash 现金 xiànjīn

to cash (cheque) 兑现(支票) duìxiàn (zhīpiào)

cash desk 现金柜台 xiànjīnguìtái

cash dispenser 自动取款机 zìdòng qǔkuǎnjī

cash machine 取钞机 qǔchāojī

cashew 腰果 yāoguǒ

cashier 收款处 shōukuǎnchù

cashmere 羊绒 yángróng

casino 赌场 dǔchǎng

casserole 沙锅 shāguō

castle 城堡 chéngbǎo

casualty department 急诊部 jízhěnbù

cat 猫 māo

catch 赶上 gǎnshang

cathedral 大教堂 dàjiàotáng

Catholic 天主教的 Tiānzhǔjiào de

cauliflower 菜花 càihuā

caution 小心 xiǎoxīn

cave 山洞 shāndòng

cavity 洞 dòng

CD 光碟 guāngdié

CD player 激光唱机 jīguāng chàngjī

CD-ROM 光盘只读存储器 guāngpán zhǐdú cúnchǔ qì

ceiling 天花板 tiānhuābǎn

celebration 庆祝 qìngzhù

celery 芹菜 qíncài

cellar 地下室 dìxiàshì

cellphone 手机 shǒujī

cemetery 墓地 mùdì

cent 分 fēn

centigrade 摄氏的 Shèshì de

centimetre 厘米 límǐ

central 中心的 zhōngxīn de

central heating 中央供暖系统 zhōngyāng gōngnuǎn xìtǒng

centre 中心 zhōngxīn

century 世纪 shìjì

the 21st century 21世纪 èrshíyī shìjì

ceramic 陶瓷的 táocí de

cereal 谷类食品 gǔlèi shípǐn

certainly 无疑地 wúyí de

certificate 证 zhèng

chain 链条 liàntiáo

chair 椅子 yǐzi

chair lift 架空吊椅 jiàkōng diàoyǐ

chairman 主席 zhǔxí

chalet 小木屋 xiǎomùwū

challenge 挑战 tiǎozhàn

chambermaid 旅馆女服务员 lǚguǎn nǚ fúwùyuán

champagne 香槟酒 xiāngbīn jiǔ

chance 可能性 kěnéngxìng

by chance 偶然 ǒurán

change 改变 gǎibiàn

to change (battery, wheel) 换 huàn
(buses, trains) 换 huàn
(money) 换(钱) huàn(qián)

changing room 试衣室 shìyīshì

channel 频道 píndào

chapel 小教堂 xiǎo jiàotáng

charcoal 木炭 mùtàn

charge (fee) 收费 shōufèi

to charge (mobile etc) 充电 chōngdiàn

free of charge 免费 miǎnfèi

charger (battery) 充电器 chōngdiàn qì

charter flight 包机 bāojī

chase 追赶 zhuīgǎn

cheap 便宜的 piányìde

check 核对 héduì

to check in (airport/hotel) 办理登机/入住手续 bànlǐ dēngjī/rùzhù shǒuxù

check-in 旅客验票台 lǚkè yànpiào tái

checkout 付款 fùkuǎn

cheek 面颊 miànjiá

cheerful 兴高采烈的 xìnggāocǎiliè de

cheers! 干杯! gānbēi!

cheese 奶酪 nǎilào

cheeseburger 干酪汉堡包 gānlào hànbāobāo

chef 厨师 chúshī

chemist's 药店 yàodiàn

cheque 支票 zhīpiào

cheque book 支票簿 zhīpiào bù

cherries 樱桃 yīngtáo

chess 象棋 xiàngqí

chest 胸腔 xiōngqiāng

chestnut 栗子 lìzi

chewing gum 口香糖 kǒuxiāngtáng

chicken 鸡 jī

chicken breast 鸡胸肉 jīxiōng ròu

chickenpox 水痘 shuǐdòu

child 孩子 háizi

children 孩子们 háizimén

child seat 儿童座 értóng zuò

chilli 辣椒 làjiāo

chilly 相当冷的 xiāngdāng lěng de

chimney 烟囱 yāncōng

chin 下巴 xiàba

china 陶瓷 táocí

China 中国 zhōngguó

Chinese (language) 汉语 hànyǔ
(person) 中国人 zhōngguórén

Chinese tea 中国茶 zhōngguóchá

chips (French fries) 炸薯条 zháshǔtiáo

chocolate 巧克力 qiǎokèlì

choice 选择 xuǎnzé

choir 合唱团 héchàngtuán

choke 阻风门 zǔfēngmén

choose 挑选 tiāoxuǎn

chop 切 qiē

chopsticks 筷子 kuàizi

christening 洗礼 xǐlǐ

Christian name 教名 jiàomíng

Christmas 圣诞节 Shèngdànjié

Merry Christmas! 圣诞快乐! Shèngdàn kuàilè!

Christmas card 圣诞卡 Shèngdàn kǎ

church 教堂 jiàotáng

chutney 酸辣酱 suānlàjiàng

cider 苹果酒 píngguǒ jiǔ

cigar 雪茄烟 xuějiā yān

cigarette 香烟 xiāngyān

cigarette lighter 打火机 dǎhuǒjī

cinema 电影院 diànyǐngyuàn

circle (theatre) 观众席 guān zhòng xi

circus 马戏团 mǎxì tuán

citizen 公民 gōngmín

city 城市 chéngshì

city centre 市中心 shì zhōngxīn

claim 声称 shēngchēng

clap 鼓掌 gǔzhǎng

clean 干净的 gānjìng de

cleaner (person) 清洁工 qīngjié gōng
(substance) 清洁剂 qīngjié jì

cleanser 洁肤霜 jiéfū shuāng

clear 明确的 míngquè de

client 顾客 gùkè

cliff 悬崖 xuányá

climate 气候 qìhòu

climb 攀登 pāndēng

clingfilm 保鲜纸 bǎoxiān zhǐ

clinic 诊所 zhěnsuǒ

cloakroom 衣帽间 yīmàojiān

clock 闹钟 nàozhōng

Cloisonné 景泰蓝 Jǐngtàilán

close 关门 guānmén

closed (door, window) 关着的 guānzhe de

(library, shop) 关闭的 guān bì de

(road) 封锁的 fēngsuǒ de

closing time 关门时间 guānmén shíjiān

cloth 布料 bùliào

clothes 衣服 yīfu

clothesline 晾衣绳 liàngyīshéng

clothes peg 晾衣夹 liàngyījiā

cloudy 多云 duōyún

clove (of garlic) 瓣 bàn

club 俱乐部 jùlèbù

clutch (car) 离合器 líhéqì

coach 长途客车 chángtúkèchē

coach trip 长途汽车旅行团 chángtú qìchē lǚxíng tuán

coal 煤 méi

coast 海岸 hǎiàn

coastguard 海岸警卫队队员 hǎiàn jǐngwèi duì duìyuán

coastline 海岸线 hǎi'àn xiàn

coat 大衣 dàyī

coat hanger 衣架 yījià

cockroach 蟑螂 zhāngláng

cocktail 鸡尾酒 jīwěijiǔ

cocoa 可可 kěkě

coconut 椰子 yēzi

coffee 咖啡 kafei

coffee (black) 咖啡不加奶 kāfēi bù jiānǎi

(instant) 速溶咖啡 sùróng kāfēi

(white) 咖啡加奶 kāfēi jiānǎi

coffee shop 咖啡店 kāfēi diàn

coin 硬币 yìngbì

Coke® 可乐 kělè

cold 冷的 lěngde

I have a cold 我感冒了 wǒ gǎnmàole

(object, water) 凉的 liáng de

(meat, room, weather) 冷的 lěng de

collar 领子 lǐngzi

collarbone 锁骨 suǒgǔ

cold water 冷水 lěngshuǐ

colleague 同事 tóngshì

collect 采集 cǎijí

(person) 接 jiē

collection (of art, stamps) 收藏品 shōucáng pǐn

collision 碰撞 pèngzhuàng

colour 颜色 yánsè

colour-blind 色盲的 sèmáng de

colour film 彩色胶卷 cǎisè jiāojuǎn

comb 梳子 shūzi

come 来 lái

come here! 到这儿来! dào zhèr lái!

come in! 请进! qǐngjìn!

comedy 幽默 yōumò

comfortable 舒服的 shūfu de

commission 佣金 yōngjīn

company 公司 gōngsī

company director 公司董事 gōngsī dǒngshì

compartment 隔间 géjiàn

compass 指南针 zhǐnánzhēn

compensation 赔偿金 péicháng jīn

compete 竞争 jìng zhēng

to complain (就某事)投诉 (jiù mǒushì) tóusù

complaint 投诉 tóusù

to complete 完全的 wánquán de

complete (building, piece of work) 完成 wánchéng

(coupon, form) 填写 tiánxiě

complication 问题 wèntí

complimentary (ticket, seat, ticket) 赠送的 zèngsòng de

composer 作曲家 zuòqǔjiā

compulsory 必须的 bìxū de

computer (language, program, system, technology etc) 电脑 diànnǎo

computer game 电脑游戏 diànnǎo yóuxì

concert 音乐会 yīnyuèhuì

concert hall 音乐厅 yīnyuètīng

concession 减价 jiǎnjià

condition 状态 zhuàngtài

condition (stipulation) 条件 tiáojiàn

conditioner 护发素 hùfàsù

condoms 避孕套 bìyuntào

conducted tour (of area)
有导游解说的旅游 yǒu dǎoyóu jiěshuō de lǚyóu

conductor 指挥家 zhǐhuījiā

confectionery 甜食 tiánshí

conference 会议 huìyì

confession 坦白 tǎnbái

confirm (appointment, date) 确认 quèrèn

(report, statement, story etc) 肯定 kěndìng

confiscate 没收 mòshōu

confused 困惑的 kùnhuò de

congestion (in nose, throat) 堵塞 dǔsè

(of road) 堵塞 dǔsè

congratulations 祝贺/恭喜 zhùhè/gōngxǐ

connection 联运 liányùn

constipated 便秘的 biànmì de

constipation 便秘 biànmì

consulate 领事馆 lǐngshì guǎn

consult 咨询 zīxún

contact 联系 liánxì

contact lenses 隐形眼镜 yǐnxíng yǎnjìng

contagious 接触传染的 jiēchù chuánrǎn de

container 容器 róngqì

continue 继续 jìxù

contraception 避孕 bìyùn

contraceptive 避孕药 bìyùn yào

contract 合同 hétóng

convenient 方便的 fāngbiàn de

cook 烹调 pēngtiáo

cooker 厨灶, 锅 chúzào, guō

cool 凉的 liáng de

copper 铜 tóng

copy (verb/noun) 复印/复印件 fùyìn/fùyìnjiàn

coriander 香菜 xiāngcài

cork 瓶塞 píngsāi

corkscrew 瓶塞钻 píngsāizuàn

corn 谷物 gǔwù

corner (of road) (路)边 (lù)biān

cornflakes 玉米片 yùmǐ piàn

coronary (coronary thrombosis)
冠心病 guànxīnbìng

corridor 走廊 zǒuláng

cosmetics 化妆品 huàzhuāngpǐn

cost 花费 huā fèi

to cost 价格 jiàgé

cot 幼儿床 yòu'ér chuáng

cottage 村舍 cūnshè

cotton 棉布 miánbù

cotton wool 脱脂棉 tuōzhī mián

cough 咳嗽 késou

cough mixture 咳嗽糖浆 késou tángjiāng

counterfeit 伪造的 wěizào de

country (nation) 国家 guójiā

countryside 农村 nóngcūn

couple (a couple of) 两个 liǎnggè

(married) 夫妻 fūqī

courgette 密生西葫芦 mìshēng xīhúlu

courier 信使 xìnshǐ

course (educational) 课程 kèchéng

first/next/last course (of meal)
第一/下一/最后一道菜 dìyī/xiàyī/zuìhòu yīdào cài

cow 奶牛 nǎiniú

crab 螃蟹 pángxiè

cranberry 越橘 yuèjú

crash 撞击 zhuàngjī

crash helmet 安全帽 ānquán mào

crayfish 鳌虾 áoxiā
cream (dairy cream) 奶油 nǎiyóu
(for skin) 乳霜 rǔshuāng
credit card 信用卡 xìnyòngkǎ
crime 罪行 zuìxíng
crisps 薯片 shǔpiàn
crop 庄稼 zhuāngjia
cross 横穿 héngchuān
cross-country 越野赛跑 yuèyě sàipǎo
crossing 横渡 héngdù
crossroads 十字路口 shízilùkǒu
crossword 填字游戏 tiánzì yóuxì
crowd 人群 rénqún
crowded 拥挤的 yōngjǐ de
crown 皇冠 huángguān
cruise 游船 yóuchuán
crutch 拐杖 guǎizhàng
cry 哭 kū
crystal 结晶体 jiéjīngtǐ
cucumber 黄瓜 huángguā
cufflinks 袖扣 xiùkòu
cuisine 烹饪 pēngrèn
cultural 文化的 wénhuà de
cumin 小茴香 xiǎohuíxiāng
cup 杯子 bēizi
cupboard 柜子 guìzi
curler 卷发夹 juǎnfà jiā
currant 无子葡萄干 wúzí pútao gān
currency 货币 huòbì
curry 咖哩 gālí
curry powder 咖哩粉 gālí fěn
curtain 窗帘 chuānglián
cushion 靠垫 kàodiàn
custard 蛋塌 dàn tǎ
custom 传统 chuántǒng
customs (duty) 海关 hǎiguān
to go through customs 过海关 guò hǎiguān
customer 顾客 gùkè
customs officer 海关官员 hǎiguān guānyuán
to cut (bread, meat) 切 qiē

to cut one's hand/knee
割破手/膝盖 gēpò shǒu/xīgài
cutlery 餐具 cānjù
cybercafe 网吧 wǎngbā
cycle 自行车 zìxíngchē
cycle hire 自行车出租 zìxíngchē chūzū
cycle lane/path 自行车道 zìxíngchēdào
cycling 骑自行车 qí zìxíngchē

D

daily 每日的 měirì de
dairy 乳制品的 rǔzhìpǐn de
dam 水坝 shuǐbà
damage 损坏 sǔnhuài
damp 潮湿的 cháoshī de
dance 舞蹈 wǔdǎo
to dance 跳舞 tiàowǔ
danger 危险 wēixiǎn
dangerous 危险的 wēixiǎn de
dark 黑暗的 hēi'àn de
date 日期 rìqī
date of birth 生日 shēngrì
daughter 女儿 nǚ'ér
daughter-in-law 儿媳妇 érxífù
dashboard 仪表板 yíbiǎobǎn
dawn 黎明 límíng
day 天 tiān
by day 在白天 zài báitiān
during the day 在白天 zài báitiān
day return 当天来回的车票 dāngtiān láihuí de chēpiào
day trip 当天来回的旅行 dāngtiān láihuí de lǚxíng
dead 死的 sǐ de
deaf 聋的 lóng de
dear (car, friend, house) 亲爱的 qīn'àide
(expensive) 昂贵的 ángguì de
death 死亡 sǐwáng
debt 债务 zhàiwù
decaffeinated 不含咖啡因的 bù hán kāfēiyīn de

December 十二月 shí'èryuè

deckchair 折叠式躺椅 zhédiéshì tǎngyǐ

to declare (at customs) 报关 bàoguān

deep 深的 shēn de

deep freeze 冷藏箱 lěngcángxiāng

deer 鹿 lù

defrost (food) 使解冻 shǐ jiědòng

delay 延误 yánwù
(on train notice boards) 误点 wùdiǎn

to be delayed (departure, flight, person) 被耽搁了 bèi dānge le

delicatessen 熟食店 shúshídiàn

delicious 美味的 měiwèi de

demonstration (protest march) 示威 shìwēi

dentist 牙医 yáyī

dentures 假牙 jiǎyá

deodorant 除臭剂 chúchòujì

to depart
(从某地)出发/出发(赶往某地)
(cóng mǒudì) chūfā/chūfā (gǎnwǎng mǒudì)

department 部 bù

department store 百货商店 bǎihuòshāngdiàn

departure lounge 候机厅 hòujītīng

departures 起飞 qǐfēi

deposit 定金 dìngjīn

describe 描述 miáoshù

description 描述 miáoshù

desk (at airport, in hotel, hospital) 服务台 fúwùtái
(in office) 办公桌 bàngōngzhuō

dessert 甜品 tiánpǐn

details 详情 xiángqíng

detergent 清洁剂 qīngjiéjì

detour 绕道 ràodào

develop 发展 fāzhǎn

diabetes 糖尿病 tāngniàobìng

diabetic 患糖尿病 huàn tángniàobìng

I'm diabetic 我是糖尿病患者 wǒ shì tángniàobìng huànzhě

to dial 拨号 bōhào

dialect 方言 fāngyán

dialling code 电话区号 diànhuà qūhào

dialling tone 拨号音 bōhàoyīn

diamond 钻石 zuànshí

diaper 尿布 niàobù

diarrhoea 腹泻 fùxiè

diary 日记簿 rìjìbù

dice 骰子 shǎizi

dictionary 字典 zìdiǎn

die (animal, person, plant) 死 sǐ

diesel 柴油 cháiyóu

diet 节食 jiéshí

to be on a diet 实行减肥节食 shíxíng jiǎnféi jiéshí

restricted food (medical) 特种饮食 tèzhǒng yǐnshí

different 不同的 bùtóng de

difficult 困难的 kùnnán de

digital camera 数码相机 shùmǎxiàngjī

digital television 数字电视 shùzì diànshì

dilute 冲淡 chōngdàn

dinghy 橡皮筏 xiàngpífá

dining room 餐厅 cāntīng

dinner (evening meal) 晚餐 wǎncān

dinner jacket 男用晚礼服 nán yòng wǎnlǐfú

diplomat 外交官 wàijiāoguān

direct (flight, route) 直达的 zhídá de

directions 方向 fāngxiàng

directory (telephone) 电话簿 diànhuàbù

directory enquiries 查号台 cháhàotái

dirty 肮脏的 āngzāngde

disability 伤残 shāngcán

disabled (person) 残疾人 cánjírén

to disagree 反对某事 fǎnduì mǒushì

disappear 消失 xiāoshī
disappointed 失望的 shīwàng de
disaster 灾难 zāinàn
disco 迪厅 dí tīng
discount 折扣 zhékòu
discover 发现 fāxiàn
disease 病 bìng
dish 盘 pán
dishcloth 擦碗布 cāwǎnbù
dishwasher 洗碗机 xīwǎnjī
dishwasher liquid 洗洁剂 xǐjiéjì
disinfectant 消毒剂 xiāodújì
disk (computer) 硬盘 yìngpán
floppy disk 软盘 ruǎnpán
dislocate (finger, jaw, shoulder etc) 使
… 脱白 shǐ … tuōjiù
disposable 一次性的 yīcìxìng de
distance 距离 jùlí
distant 远的 yuǎn de
distilled (water, whisky) 蒸馏
zhēngliú
district 地区 dìqū
disturb 打扰 dǎrǎo
dive (into water) 跳水 tiàoshuǐ
diver 潜水员 qiánshuǐyuán
diversion 临时改道 línshí gǎidào
diving 潜水 qiánshuǐ
distributor (part of car) 分销商
fēnxiāoshāng
divorced 离婚了 líhūn le
to get divorced 离婚 líhūn
DIY 自己动手的 zìjǐ dòngshǒu de
dizzy 感到头晕 gǎndào tóuyūn
do 做 zuò
doctor 医生 yīshēng
documents 文件 wénjiàn
dog 狗 gǒu
doll 娃娃 wáwa
dollar 元 yuán
domestic (flights) 国内的 guónèide
dominoes 多米诺骨牌 duōmǐnuò
gǔpái
donor card 器官捐献卡 qìguān
juānxiànkǎ

door 门 mén
doorbell 门铃 ménlíng
double 双人 shuāngrén
double bed 双人床
shuāngrénchuáng
double room 双人房
shuāngrénfáng
doughnut 炸面包圈 zhá
miànbāoquān
down 下 xià
downstairs 楼下 lóuxià
dragonfly 蜻蜓 qīngtíng
drain (in street) 排水沟 páishuǐgōu
draught (of air) 气流 qìliú
draught beer 散装的 sǎnzhuāng
de
drawer 抽屉 chōuti
drawing 素描 sùmiáo
dress 连衣裙 liányīqún
to dress (oneself) 穿好衣服
chuānhǎo yīfu
dressing (salad) 调料 tiáoliào
(on a wound) 敷料 fūliào
dressing gown 晨衣 chényī
drill (tool) 钻 zuàn
drink (soft) 饮料 yǐnliào
drinking water 饮用水
yǐnyòngshuǐ
drive 车程 chēchéng
driver (of car) 司机 sījī
driving licence 驾驶证
jiàshǐzhèng
drizzle 蒙蒙细雨 méngméng xìyǔ
drought 旱灾 hànzāi
drown 使淹死 shǐ yānsǐ
drug (medicine) 药 yào
(narcotics) 毒品 dúpǐn
drunk 醉汉 zuìhàn
dry 干的 gān de
dry-cleaner's 干洗店 gānxǐdiàn
dryer (spin-dryer, tumble dryer)
干衣机 gānyījī
duck 鸭 yā
due 应到 yīng dào

dummy (for baby) 橡皮奶头
  xiàngpí nǎitóu
during 在 ··· 期间 zài ... qījiān
dust 灰尘 huīchén
dustbin 垃圾箱 lājīxiāng
duster 抹布 mābù
duty (tax) 税 shuì
duty-free 免税 miǎnshuì
duty-free shops 免税店
  miǎnshuìdiàn
duvet 羽绒被 yǔróngbèi
dye 染料 rǎnliào

E

each 每 měi
eagle 鹰 yīng
ear 耳朵 ěrduo
earache 耳朵痛 ěrduo tòng
earlier 较早的 jiàozǎo de
early 在初期 zài chūqī
earphones 耳机 ěrjī
earplugs 耳塞 ěrsāi
earrings 耳环 ěrhuán
earth (planet) 地球 dìqiú
earthquake 地震 dìzhèn
east 东方 dōngfāng
Easter 复活节 fùhuójié
Happy Easter! 复活节快乐! Fùhuó
  Jié kuàilè!
easy 容易的 róngyì de
to eat 吃 chī
echo 回音 huíyīn
economy 经济 jīngjì
edge 边缘 biānyuán
eel 鳗鱼 mànyú
effective 有效的 yǒuxiào de
egg 蛋 dàn
egg white 蛋白 dànbái
egg yolk 蛋黄 dànhuáng
eight 八 bā
eighteen 十八 shíbā
eighth 第八 dìbā
eighty 八十 bāshí
either 两者任一的 liǎngzhě rènyī de

elastic band 橡皮筋 xiàngpíjīn
elbow 肘 zhǒu
electric 电动的 diàndòng de
electric blanket 电热毯 diànrètǎn
electric point 电源 diànyuán
electrician 电工 diàngōng
electricity 电 diàn
electricity meter 量电计
  liángdiànjì
electricity razor 电动剃须刀
  diàndòng tìxūdāo
electricity shock 触电 chùdiàn
elegant 优雅的 yōuyǎ de
elevator 电梯 diàntī
eleven 十一 shíyī
e-mail 电子邮件 diànzǐyóujiàn
e-mail address 电子邮件地址
  diànzǐ yóujiàn dizhǐ
embarrassing 令人尴尬的 lìng
  rén gāngà de
embassy 大使馆 dàshǐguǎn
emergency 紧急事件 jǐnjíshìjiàn
emergency exit 紧急出口
  jǐnjíchūkǒu
empty 空的 kōng de
end 末期 mòqī
engaged (to be married) 已订婚的
  yǐ dìnghūn de
(toilet) 被占用的 bèi zhànyòng de
engine 发动机 fādòngjī
engineer 工程师 gōngchéngshī
England 英格兰 yīnggélán
English (person) 英国人
  yīngguórén
(language) 英语 yīngyǔ
Englishman 英格兰男人
  Yīnggélán nánrén
Englishwoman 英格兰女人
  Yīnggélán nǚrén
enjoy oneself 过得快活 guòde
  kuàihuó
enjoy your meal! 请慢用! qǐng
  màn yòng
enlarge 扩大 kuòdà

enormous 庞大的 pángdà de
enough 足够的 zúgòu de
that's enough! 够了！gòule!
enter 进入 jìnrù
entertainment 娱乐活动 yúlèhuódòng
enthusiastic 极感兴趣的 jí gǎn xìngqù de
entrance 入口 rùkǒu
entrance fee 入场费 rùchǎngfèi
envelope 信封 xìnfēng
epilepsy 癫痫 diānxián
epileptic fit 癫痫发作 diānxián fāzuò
equipment 设备 shèbèi
eraser 橡皮擦 xiàngpí cā
error 差错 chācuò
eruption (volcano) 喷发 pēnfā
escalator 自动扶梯 zìdòng fútī
to escape (to safety) 安全逃走 ānquán táozǒu
essential 必要的 bìyào de
establish 建立 jiànlì
estate agent 房地产经纪 人 fángdìchǎn jīngjìrén
euro 欧元 Ōuyuán
Europe 欧洲 ōuzhōu
European 欧洲的 Ōuzhōu de
European Union 欧洲联盟 Ōuzhōu Liánméng
eve 在 ··· 的前夕 zài ... de qiánxī
even (number) 偶数的 ǒushù de
evening 晚上 wǎnshàng
this evening 今晚 jīnwǎn
tomorrow evening 明晚 míngwǎn
evening dress 女装晚礼服 nǚzhuāng wǎnlǐfú
every 每个 měigè
everybody 每人 měirén
everything 所有事物 suǒyǒu shìwù
everywhere 各处 gèchù
examination 检查 jiǎnchá
example: *for example* 例如 lìrú

excellent 极好的 jíhǎo de
except 除了 chúle
excess baggage 超重行李 chāozhòng xíngli
to exchange 用某物交换 yòng mǒuwù jiāohuàn
exchange rate 兑换率 duìhuànlǜ
exciting 令人兴奋的 lìng rén xīngfèn de
excursion 游览 yóulǎn
excuse 借口 jièkǒu
excuse me! (sorry) 对不起！ duìbùqǐ!
(when passing) 请让一让！qǐng ràngyīràng!
exercise (physical) 运动 yùndòng
exercise book 练习本 liànxíběn
exhaust (car) 废气 fèiqì
exhibition 展览 zhǎnlǎn
exit 出口 chūkǒu
expenses 经费 jīngfèi
expensive 昂贵的 ángguìde
expert 专家 zhuānjiā
expire (licence, passport) 过期 guòqī
expiry date 到期日 dàoqīrì
explain 解释 jiěshì
explosion 爆炸 bàozhà
export 输出 shūchū
express (coach, train) 快车 kuàichē
extension (electrical) 延长部分 yáncháng bùfen
extra 额外的 éwài de
extinguish 扑灭 pūmiè
eye 眼睛 yǎnjīng
eyebrow 眉毛 méimao
eyedrops 眼药水 yǎnyàoshuǐ
eyelash 眼睫毛 yǎnjiémáo
eyeliner 眼线笔 yǎnxiànbǐ
eyeshadow 眼影 yǎnyǐng

F

fabric 织物 zhīwù
face 脸 liǎn
facecloth 洗脸毛巾 xǐliǎn máojīn

facial 面部的 miànbù de

facility 设施 shèshī

factory 工厂 gōngchǎng

fail 没有通过 méiyǒu tōngguò

to feel faint 感到眩晕 gǎndào xuànyūn

fair (hair) 金色的 jīnsè de

(funfair) 游乐场 yóulèchǎng

(just) 公平的 gōngpíng de

(trade) 交易会 jiāoyìhuì

fake 假货 jiǎhuò

fall (autumn) 秋天 qiūtiān

to fall 掉 diào

false teeth 假牙 jiǎ yá

family 家庭 jiātíng

famous 著名的 zhùmíng de

fan (admirer) 粉丝 fěnsī

(electric) 风扇 fēngshàn

(handheld) 扇子 shànzī

fancy dress 奇装异服 qízhuāngyìfú

far 远的 yuǎn de

how far? 多远? duōyuǎn?

fare (bus, train etc) 票价 piàojià

farm 农场 nóngchǎng

farmer 农民 nóngmín

farmhouse 农舍 nóngshè

fashionable 时尚的 shí shàng de

fast 快的 kuài de

fasten 固定 gùdìng

fat 肥胖的 féipàng de

(for cooking) 食用油 shíyòng yóu

father 父亲 fùqin

father-in-law 公公 gōnggong

fault (defect) 故障 gùzhàng

it's my fault 是我的错 shì wǒde cuò

favour 赞成 zànchéng

favourite 最喜欢的 zuì xǐhuan de

fax 传真 chuánzhēn

feather 羽毛 yǔmáo

February 二月 èryuè

feed 喂 wèi

feel 摸 mō

I don't feel well 我觉得身体不适 wǒ juéde shēntǐ bùshì

feet 脚 jiǎo

fellow 小伙子 xiǎohuǒzi

female 女的 nǚde

ferry 渡船 dùchuán

festival 节日 jiérì

to fetch (to bring) 去拿来 qù nálái

(to go and get) 去给某人拿来某物 qù gěi mǒurén nálái mǒuwù

fever 发烧 fāshāo

few 少数的 shǎoshù de

a few 几个 jǐge

fiancé(e) 未婚夫/妻 wèihūnfū/qī

field 草地 cǎodì

fifteen 十五 shíwǔ

fifth 第五 dìwǔ

fifty 五十 wǔshí

fig 无花果 wúhuāguǒ

fight 斗殴 dòu'ōu

to fight 跟某人打架 gēn mǒurén dǎjià

file (computer) 文件 wénjiàn

(dossier) 档案 dàng'àn

(folder) 文件夹 wénjiànjiā

to fill 用某物填满某物 yòng mǒuwù tiánmǎn mǒuwù

fill it up! 请加满油 qǐng jiāmǎn yóu

to fill in (form) 填写 tiánxiě

fillet 片 piàn

filling (in tooth) 填补物 tiánbǔ wù

filling station 加油站 jiāyóu zhàn

film (at cinema) 电影 diànyǐng

(for camera) 胶卷 jiāojuǎn

filter 过滤器 guòlǜ qì

find 找到 zhǎodào

fine 还不错的 hái bùcuò de

fine art 美术 měishù

finger 手指 shǒuzhǐ

finish 结束 jiéshù

fire 火 huǒ

fire! 着火了! zháohuǒle!

fire alarm 火警报警器 huǒjǐng

bàojǐngqì

fire brigade 消防队 xiāofángduì

fire engine 救火车 jiùhuǒchē

fire escape 消防出口 xiāofáng chū kǒu

fire extinguisher 灭火器 mièhuǒqì

firemen 消防员 xiāofángyuán

fireplace 壁炉 bìlú

firework 烟火 yānhuǒ

firm (company) 公司 gōngsī

first 第一 dìyī

first aid 急救 jíjiù

first-aid kit 急救包 jíjiùbāo

first class 一等舱/一等车厢 yīděngcāng/yīděngchēxiāng

first name 名 míng

fish 鱼 yú

to go fishing 去钓鱼 qù diàoyú

fisherman 渔民 yúmín

fishing boat 渔船 yúchuán

fishing rod 钓竿 diàogān

fishmonger 鱼贩 yúfàn

fit: *to be a good fit* 很合身 hěn héshēn

five 五 wǔ

to fix 修理 xiūlǐ

fizzy 带气的 dàiqì de

flag 旗 qí

flame 火焰 huǒyàn

flash (for camera) 闪光灯 shǎnguāngdēng

flashlight 手电筒 shǒudiàn tǒng

flask 保温瓶 bǎowēnpíng

flat (apartment) 公寓 gōngyù

(ball, tyre) 气不足的 qì bùzú de

(battery) 没电的 méidiàn de

(ground, surface) 平的 píng de

flavour 味 wèi

flaw (in cloth, pattern) 毛病 máobìng

flea 跳蚤 tiàozao

fleece (garment) 毛呢衣物 máoní yīwù

flesh 肉 ròu

flex 电线 diànxiàn

flight 航班 hángbān

flip-flops 夹趾拖鞋 jiāzhǐ tuōxié

flipper (for swimming) 脚蹼 jiǎopǔ

flood 洪水 hóngshuǐ

floor 地板 dìbǎn

(storey) 楼层 lóucéng

ground floor 一楼 yīlóu

floppy disk 软盘 ruǎnpán

florist's shop 花店 huādiàn

flour 面粉 miánfěn

flowers 花 huā

flu 流感 liúgǎn

fly 苍蝇 cāngying

to fly 飞 fēi

fog 雾 wù

foggy 有雾的 yǒuwù de

foil (kitchen) 箔纸 bózhǐ

follow 跟随 gēnsuí

food 食物 shíwù

food poisoning 食物中毒 shíwùzhòngdú

fool 白痴 báichī

foot 脚 jiǎo

on foot 步行 bùxíng

football 足球 zúqiú

footballer 足球运动员 zúqiú yùndòngyuán

football match 足球赛 zúqiú sài

footpath 人行小径 rénxíng xiǎojìng

for 为 wèi

forbidden 被禁止的 bèi jìnzhǐ de

forehead 额 é

foreign 外国的 wàiguó de

foreigner 外国人 wàiguórén

forest 森林 sēnlín

forever 永远 yǒngyuǎn

to forget 忘记 wàng jì

forgive 原谅 yuánliàng

fork (for eating) 叉 chā

(in road, railway, river) 岔路 chàlù

form (document) 表格 biǎogé

154

formal dress 礼服 lǐfú
fortnight 两星期 liǎng xīngqī
fortress 堡垒 bǎolěi
forty 四十 sìshí
forward 向前的 xiàngqián de
foul play (in sport) 犯规行为 fànguī xíngwéi
fountain 喷泉 pēnquán
four 四 sì
fourteen 十四 shísì
fourth 第四 dìsì
four-wheel drive 四轮驱动 sìlún qūdòng
fox 狐狸 húli
fracture 断裂 duànliè
fragile 纤巧的 xiānqiǎo de
fragrance 香气 xiāngqì
frame (mirror, picture etc) 框 kuàng
France 法国 Fǎguó
free (costing nothing) 免费的 miǎnfèi de
freezer 冰柜 bīngguì
French (language) 法语 Fǎyǔ
(person) 法国人 Fǎguórén
French bean 菜豆 càidòu
French fries 炸薯条 zhá shǔtiáo
frequent 频繁的 pínfán de
fresh 新鲜的 xīnxiān de
freshwater 淡水的 dànshuǐ de
Friday 星期五 xīngqīwǔ
fridge 冰箱 bīngxiāng
fried 炒的 chǎo de
friend 朋友 péngyou
friendly 友善的 yǒushàn de
frog 青蛙 qīngwā
from 来自 láizì
front 前面 qiánmiàn
in front of 在 … 前面 zài … qiánmiàn
front door 前门 qiánmén
frost 霜 shuāng
frozen 冷冻的 lěngdòng de
fruit 水果 shuǐguǒ
fruit juice 果汁 guǒzhī

fruit salad 水果色拉 shuǐguǒ sèlā
fruit shop 水果店 shuǐguǒdiàn
fry 油煎 yóujiān
frying pan 平底煎锅 píngdǐ jiānguō
fuel 燃料 ránliào
full 满的 mǎn de
I'm full (up) 我吃饱了 wǒ chībǎo le
fumes (of car, fire, fuel) 浓烈的烟气 nóngliè de yānqì
fun 乐趣 lèqù
funeral 葬礼 zànglǐ
funfair 露天游乐场 lùtiān yóulèchǎng
funny 可笑的 kěxiào de
(strange) 奇怪的 qíguài de
fur 毛 máo
furnish 布置 bùzhì
furniture 家具 jiājù
fuse 保险丝 bǎoxiǎnsī
fuse box 保险丝盒 bǎoxiǎnsī hé
future 未来 wèilái

G

gallery (art) 美术馆 měishùguǎn
gallon 加仑 jiālún
game 游戏 yóuxì
garage (private) 车库 chēkù
(for petrol) 加油站 jiāyóuzhàn
(for repairs) 汽车修理厂 qìchē xiūlǐchǎng
garden 花园 huāyuán
gardener 园丁 yuándīng
garlic 大蒜 dàsuàn
garnish 加饰菜于 jiā shìcài yú
gas 煤气 méiqì
gas cooker 煤气炉 méiqìlú
gas cylinder 煤气罐 méiqìguàn
gate (airport) 登机口 dēngjīkǒu
gay (person) 欢快的 huānkuài de
gear box 变速箱 biànsùxiāng
gears 汽车排档 qìchē páidǎng
generous 大方的 dàfang de

gents' (toilet) 男厕所 náncèsuǒ

genuine (antique, leather etc) 真正的 zhēnzhèng de

German (language) 德语 Déyǔ

(person) 德国人 Déguórén

German measles 风疹 fēngzhěn

Germany 德国 Déguó

to get (to fetch) 去拿 qùná

(to obtain) 获得 huòdé

(to receive) 收到 shōudào

to get off (vehicle) 下车 xiàchē

gift 礼物 lǐwù

gift shop 礼品店 lǐpǐndiàn

gin 杜松子酒 dùsōngzǐjiǔ

ginger 姜 jiāng

girl 女孩 nǚhái

girlfriend 女朋友 nǚpéngyou

to give 给某人某物 gěi mǒurén mǒuwù

to give back 把某物交还给某人 bǎ mǒuwù jiāohuán gěi mǒurén

glacier 冰川 bīngchuān

glass (for drinking) 玻璃杯 bōlíbēi

a glass of water 一杯水 yī bēi shuǐ

a glass of wine 一杯葡萄酒 yī bēi pútaojiǔ

(substance) 玻璃 bōlí

glasses 眼镜 yǎnjìng

gloss 光泽 guāngzé

glove 手套 shǒutào

glue 胶 jiāo

to go 去 qù

I'm going to... 我正要去… wǒ zhèng yào qù…

we're going to... 我们正要去… wǒ men zhèng yào qù…

to go back 返回 fǎnhuí

to go down 下降 xiàjiàng

to go in 进去 jìnqù

goat 山羊 shānyáng

God 上帝 Shàngdì

godchild 教子 jiàozǐ

goggles 护目镜 hùmùjìng

gold 黄金 huángjīn

golf 高尔夫球 gāo'ěrfūqiú

golf ball 高尔夫球 gāo'ěrfūqiú

golf club 高尔夫球棍 gāo'ěrfūqiúgùn

golf course 高尔夫球场 gāo'ěrfūqiúchǎng

good 好 hǎo

goodbye 再见 zàijiàn

good evening! 晚上好! wǎnshàng hǎo!

good morning/afternoon! 早上/下午好! zǎoshàng/xiàwǔ hǎo!

good night 晚安 wǎnān

goose 鹅 é

graduate 毕业生 bìyèshēng

gram 克 kè

grapes 葡萄 pútao

grass 草 cǎo

grated (cheese etc) 磨碎 mósuì

grater (for cheese etc) 磨碎器 mósuìqì

greasy (food) 油腻的 yóunì de

great (large) 巨大的 jùdà de

(place, terrific person) 好极了的 hǎojíle de

Great Britain 大不列颠 Dàbùlièdiān

green (colour) 绿色 lǜsè

green card 绿卡 lǜkǎ

greengrocer's 果蔬店 guǒshūdiàn

green tea 绿茶 lǜchá

greetings card 贺卡 hèkǎ

grill 烤架 kǎojià

to grill 烤 kǎo

grey 灰色 huīsè

grocer's 杂货店 záhuòdiàn

ground (earth, soil) 土地 tǔdì

(floor) 地面 dìmiàn

ground floor 一楼 yī lóu

groundsheet 铺地防潮布 pūdì fángcháobù

group 组 zǔ

guarantee 保证 bǎozhèng

guard 警卫 jǐngwèi

guest 客人 kèrén

(in hotel) 房客 fángkè

guesthouse 招待所 zhāodàisuǒ

guide (tourist) 导游 dǎoyóu

guidebook 导游册 dǎoyóucè

guided tour 有导游的游览 yǒu dǎoyóu de yóulǎn

guitar 吉他 jítā

gun 枪 qiāng

gym 健身房 jiànshēnfáng

gym shoes 体操鞋 tǐcāoxié

H

haemorrhoids 痔疮 zhìchuāng

hail 冰雹 bīngbáo

(taxi) 打的 dǎdī

hair 头发 tóufa

hairbrush 发刷 fàshuā

haircut 理发 lǐfà

hairdresser's 美发师 měifàshī

hairdryer 吹风机 chuīfēngjī

hair gel 发胶 fàjiāo

hairspray 喷雾发胶 pēnwù fàjiāo

hake 狗鳕 gǒuxuě

half 一半 yíbàn

half an hour 半小时 bàn xiǎoshí

half a pound/kilo/mile 半磅/公斤/英里 bànbàng/gōngjīn/yīnglǐ

half fare 半票 bànpiào

half-price 半价 bànjià

ham (joint, meat) 火腿 huǒtuǐ

hamburger 汉堡包 hànbǎobāo

hammer 锤子 chuízi

hand 手 shǒu

handbag 手提包 shǒutíbāo

handbrake 手闸 shǒuzhá

handicapped 有残疾 yǒucánjí

handkerchief 手帕 shǒupà

handle (of cup) 柄 bǐng

(of door, window) 拉手 lāshǒu

handlebars 把手 bǎshǒu

hand luggage 手提行李 shǒutí xíngli

handmade 手工制作的 shǒugōng zhìzuò de

hands-free kit 手机车载免提套件 shǒujī chēzài miǎntí tàojiàn

handsome (man) 英俊的 yīngjùn de

(woman) 健美的 jiànměi de

to hang up (clothes, picture etc) 挂 guà

hanger 衣架 yījià

hang-gliding 悬挂式滑翔运动 xuánguàshì huáxiáng yùndòng

hangover 宿醉 sùzuì

to happen 发生 fāshēng

what will happen if...? 如果 … 会怎么样? rúguǒ … huì zěnmeyàng?

happy 快乐 kuàilè

Happy Anniversary! 纪念日快乐! jìniànrì kuàilè!

Happy Birthday! 生日快乐! shēngrì kuàilè!

Happy Easter! 复活节快乐! fùhuójié kuàilè!

Happy New Year! 新年快乐! xīnnián kuàilè!

harbour 港口 gǎngkǒu

hard 硬的 yìng de

(not easy) 困难的 kùnnan de

hard disk 硬盘 yìngpán

hardware store 五金商店 wǔjīn shāngdiàn

hare 野兔 yětù

harm 损坏 sǔnhuài

harvest 收获 shōuhuò

hat 帽子 màozi

to have 有 yǒu

I have... 我有 … wǒ yǒu…

we have... 我们有 … wǒmen yǒu…

hay fever 花粉热 huāfěn rè

hazelnut 榛子 zhēnzi

he 他 tā

head 头 tóu

headache 头疼 tóuténg

to have a headache 头痛 tóutòng

headlights 车头灯 chētóudēng

headphones 耳机 ěrjī

health 健康 jiànkāng

health food 保健食品 bǎojiàn
shípǐn

healthy 健康的 jiànkāng de

hear 听见 tīngjiàn

hearing aid 助听器 zhùtīngqì

heart 心 xīn

heart attack 心脏病发作
xīnzàngbìng fāzuò

heartbeat 心跳 xīntiào

heartburn 胃灼热 wèizhuórè

heart disease 心脏病
xīnzàngbìng

heat 热 rè

heater 供暖装置 gōngnuǎn
zhuāngzhì

heating 暖气 nuǎnqì

heaven 天堂 tiāntáng

heavy 重的 zhòng de

heel (of foot) 脚后跟 jiǎohòugēn
(of shoe) 鞋跟 xiégēn

height 高度 gāodù

helicopter 直升飞机 zhíshēng
fēijī

hello! 你好! nǐhǎo!

hello (on phone) 喂 wèi

helmet 头盔 tóukuī

help! 救命啊! jiùmìng a!

to help 帮助 bāngzhù

can you help me? 你能帮助我吗?
nǐ néng bāngzhù wǒ ma?

hem 褶边 zhěbiān

hen 母鸡 mǔjī

hepatitis 肝炎 gānyán

her 她的 tāde

herb 草本植物 cǎoběn zhíwù

herbal tea 药茶 yàochá

here 在这里 zài zhèlǐ

here is... 这里是… zhèlǐ shì...

here is my passport 这是我的护照
zhè shì wǒ de hùzhào

hernia 疝 shàn

hi! 嘿! heì!

to hide (oneself) 躲(某人) duǒ
(something) 藏(某物) cáng

high (building, heel, wall, price, speed,
temperature etc) 高的 gāo de

highchair 高脚椅 gāojiǎoyǐ

hill 小山 xiǎoshān

hill-walking 登山 dēngshān

him 他 tā

hip 臀部 túnbù

hire (car) 租借车 zūjièchē

his 他的 tāde

historic 历史性的 lìshǐxìng de

history 历史 lìshǐ

to hit 打 dǎ

to hitchhike 搭便车旅行 dā
biànchē lǚxíng

HIV 艾滋病毒 àizībìng bìngdú

to be HIV positive/negative
携带艾滋病毒/未受艾滋病毒
感染 xiédài Aìzībìng
bìngdú/wèishòu Aìzībìng bìngdú
gǎnrǎn

hobby 爱好 àihào

to hold (contain) 容纳 róngnà

hold-up (in traffic) 交通阻塞
jiāotōng zǔsè

hole 洞 dòng

holiday 度假 dùjià
(public) 公共假期 gōnggòng jiàqī

to be on holiday 在度假 zài dùjià

holiday resort 旅游胜地 lǚyóu
shèngdì

hollow 空的 kōng de

holy (person) 圣洁的 shèngjié de
(place, picture, water) 神圣的
shénshèng de

home 家 jiā

at home 在家 zàijiā

to go home 回家 huí

homesick 想家的 xiǎngjiā de

homosexual 同性恋的 tóngxìngliàn de

honest 诚实的 chéngshí de

honey 蜂蜜 fēngmì

honeymoon 蜜月 mìyuè

Hong Kong 香港 Xiānggǎng

hood (of car) 发动机罩 fādòngjī zhào

(of coat etc) 兜帽 dōumào

hook (for coats, fishing etc) 钩 gōu

to hope 盼望 pànwàng

I hope so/not
希望是这样/希望不会 xīwàng shì zhèyàng/xīwàng bùhuì

horn (of car) 喇叭 lǎba

hors d'oeuvre 餐前的开胃小吃 cānqián de kāiwèi xiǎochī

horse 马 mǎ

horse racing 赛马 sàimǎ

horse riding 骑马 qímǎ

hosepipe 输水软管 shūshuǐ ruǎnguǎn

hospital 医院 yīyuàn

hostel 招待所 zhāodàisuǒ

hot 热 rè

hot chocolate 热巧克力 rè qiǎokèlì

hotel 旅馆 lǚguǎn

hot water 热水 rèshuǐ

hot-water bottle 热水袋 rèshuǐdài

hour 小时 xiǎoshí

house 家 jiā

housewife 家庭主妇 jiātíng zhǔfù

housewine
饭馆酒吧提供的最便宜的葡萄酒 fànguǎn, jiǔbā tígōng de zuì piányi de pútáojiǔ

housework 家务劳动 jiāwù láodòng

hovercraft 气垫船 qìdiàn chuán

how 怎样 zěnyàng

how are you? 你好吗? nǐ hǎo ma?

how much? 多少钱? duōshǎo qián?

how much is it? 多少钱? duōshǎo qián?

hundred 百 bǎi

hungry 饿 è

hunt 打猎 dǎliè

to hunt 打猎 dǎliè

hurry 赶紧 gǎnjǐn

to be in a hurry (to do something) 急于 (做某事) jí yú (zuò mǒushì)

to hurt 弄痛 nòngtòng

that hurts 痛 tòng

husband 丈夫 zhàngfu

hut 简陋的小屋 jiǎnlòu de xiǎowū

hydrofoil 水翼船 shuǐyì chuán

I

I 我 wǒ

ice 冰 bīng

(for drink) 冰块 bīngkuài

ice cream 冰淇淋 bīngqílín

ice rink 溜冰场 liūbīngchǎng

ice-skating 溜冰 liūbīng

idea 主意 zhǔyì

identity card 身份证 shēnfènzhèng

if 如果 rǔguǒ

ignition 点火 diánhuǒ

ill 生病 shēngbìng

I'm ill 我病了 wǒ bìngle

illness 病 bìng

immediately 立即地 lìjí de

immigration 移民 yímín

immunize 使免疫 shǐ miǎnyì

to import 进口 jìnkǒu

important 重要的 zhòngyào de

impossible 无法忍受的 wúfǎ rěnshòu de

to improve 改善 gǎishàn

in 在 … 里 zài … lǐ

(within) 在 … 之后 zài … zhīhòu

in London/England
在伦敦/英格兰 zài Lúndūn/Yīnggélán

inch 英寸 yīngcùn

included 包括在内的 bāokuò zàinèi de
inconvenient 不方便的 bù fāng biàn de
to increase 增长 zēngzhǎng
indicator (on car) 显示器 xiǎnshìqì
indigestion 消化不良 xiāohuà bù liáng
indoors 在室内 zài shì nèi
inefficient 效率低的 xiàolǜ dī de
infection 炎症 yánzhèng
infectious 传染的 chuánrǎn de
informal (clothes, party) 日常的 rìcháng de
(person) 不拘礼节的 bùjū lǐjié de
information 信息 xìn xī
ingredient 成分 chéngfèn
inhaler 吸入器 xīrùqì
injection 注射 zhùshè
injure (oneself) 伤害（自己）shāng hài
injured 受伤的 shòushāng de
injury 伤害 shānghài
ink 墨水 mòshuǐ
inn 小旅馆 xiǎo lǚguǎn
inquiry 询问 xúnwèn
insect 昆虫 kūnchóng
insect repellent 杀虫剂 shāchóngjì
inside 内部 nèibù
instalment 分期付款 fēnqī fùkuǎn
instant coffee 速溶咖啡 sù róng kā fēi
instead of 而不是 ér bùshì
instructor 教员 jiàoyuán
insulin 胰岛素 yídǎosù
insurance 保险 bǎoxiǎn
fully comprehensive insurance 全保险 quán bǎoxiǎn
insurance policy 保险单 bǎoxiǎndān
to insure 给 … 保险 gěi … bǎoxiǎn
intelligent 聪明的 cōngming de

to intend to (do something) 打算做某事 dǎsuàn zuò mǒushì
interesting 有趣的 yǒuqù de
internet 因特网 yīntèwǎng
internet café 网吧 wǎngbā
international 国际的 guójìde
interpreter 口译者 kǒuyìzhě
interval 间隔 jiàngé
interview 面试 miànshì
into 到 … 里面 dào … lǐmiàn
let's go into town 我们进城吧 wǒmen jìnchéng ba
to introduce somebody to somebody 给某人介绍(某人) gěi mǒurén jièshào (mǒurén)
invitation 邀请 yāoqǐng
to invite 邀请 yāoqǐng
Ireland 爱尔兰 Ài'ěrlán
Irish 爱尔兰的 Ài'ěrlán de
iron (for clothes) 熨斗 yùndǒu
(metal) 铁 tiě
to do the ironing 熨衣服 yùn yīfu
ironing board 熨衣板 yùnyībǎn
island 岛 dǎo
Italian (language) 意大利语 Yìdàlìyǔ
(person) 意大利人 Yìdàlìrén
Italy 意大利 Yìdàlì
to itch 发痒 fāyǎng
it's itchy 发痒的 fāyǎng de
item (on bill) 项目 xiàng mù
ivory 象牙 xiàngyá

J

jack (for car) 千斤顶 qiānjīndǐng
jacket 夹克衫 jiākèshān
jackpot 头彩 tóucǎi
jade 玉石 yùshí
jam (food) 果酱 guǒjiàng
jammed (roads) 堵塞的 dǔsè de
January 一月 yīyuè
Japan 日本 Rìběn
Japanese (language) 日语 Rìyǔ
(person) 日本人 Rìběnrén

jar 广口瓶 guǎngkǒupíng
jaw 颌 hé
jazz 爵士乐 juéshìyuè
jealous 妒忌的 dùjì de
jeans 牛仔裤 niúzǎikù
jelly (dessert) 果冻 guǒdòng
jellyfish 海蜇 hǎizhé
jet engine 喷气发动机 pēnqì
fādòngjī
jetty 码头 mǎtóu
jewel 宝石 bǎoshí
jeweller's 珠宝店 zhūbǎodiàn
jewellery 珠宝 zhūbǎo
Jewish 犹太人 Yóutàirén
job 工作 gōngzuò
to jog 慢跑 mànpǎo
to join (club, party etc) 加入 jiārù
(connect) 连接 liánjiē
joint (of body) 关节 guānjié
joke 笑话 xiàohua
to joke 开玩笑 kāiwánxiào
journalist 记者 jìzhě
journey 旅程 lǚchéng
judge (estimate) 判断 pànduàn
jug 壶 hú
juice 汁 zhī
July 七月 qīyuè
to jump (into air) 跳 tiào
jumper 毛衣 máo yī
junction 交叉点 tiào
June 六月 jiāochādiǎn
just 只是 zhǐshì
I'm just finishing this
我马上就做完了 wǒ mǎshàng jiù
zuòwán le

K

karaoke 卡拉OK kǎlā ōukèi
karate 空手道 kōngshǒudào
to keep (retain) 保留 bǎoliú
(store) 保存 bǎocún
keep out 止步 zhǐbù
kennel 狗窝 gǒuwō
kettle 水壶 shuǐhú

key 钥匙 yàoshi
keyboard 键盘 jiànpán
keyring 钥匙环 yàoshihuán
to kick (ball, person) 踢 tī
kid (child) 小孩 xiǎohái
kidney 肾脏 shènzàng
to kill 杀死 shāsǐ
kilogram 公斤 gōngjīn
kilometre 公里 gōnglǐ
kind (person) 友善的 yǒushànde
(sort, type) 种类 zhǒnglèi
king 国王 guówáng
kiss 吻 wěn
to kiss 接吻 jiēwěn
kitchen 厨房 chúfáng
kitchen sink 厨房洗涤池 chúfáng
xǐdíchí
kite 风筝 fēngzheng
kitten 小猫 xiǎomāo
kiwi fruit 猕猴桃 míhóutáo
knife 刀 dāo
to knit 织 zhī
to knock (on door) 敲(门) qiāo
(mén)
to knock down (with car) 撞倒
zhuàngdǎo
to knock over (something) 撞倒
zhuàngdǎo
knot 结 jié
to know (facts) 知道 zhīdào
(person, place) 认识 rènshi
do you know how to swim?
你会游泳吗? nǐ huì yóuyǒng ma?
I don't know 我不知道 wǒ bù
zhīdào

L

label 标签 biāoqiān
lace (fabric) 花边 huābiān
(of shoe) 系带 jìdài
ladder 梯子 tīzi
ladies (toilet) 女厕所 nǚcèsuǒ
lady 女士 nǚshì
lake 湖 hú

lamb 羔羊 gāoyáng

lame 跛的 bǒ de

lamp 台灯 táidēng

lamp-post 路灯柱 lùdēngzhù

lampshade 灯罩 dēngzhào

land (country) 国家 guójiā

(ground) 土地 tǔdì

to land (on dry ground) 上岸 shàng àn

landing (of plane) 使降落 shǐ jiàngluò

landing card 入境登记卡 rùjìng dēngjìkǎ

landlady 女房东 nǚfángdōng

landlord 男房东 nánfángdōng

landslide 塌方 tāfāng

lane (of road) 车道 chēdào

language 语言 yǔyán

laptop (computer) 笔记本电脑 bǐjìběn diànnǎo

large 大的 dà de

last 最后的 zuìhòu de

last night 昨晚 zuówǎn

last week 上个星期 shàng gè xīngqī

late 迟的 chí de

sorry I'm late 对不起，我迟到了 duìbuqǐ, wǒ chídào le

we're late 我们迟到了 wǒmen chídào le

later 以后 yǐ hòu

to laugh 笑 xiào

laundrette 自助洗衣店 zìzhù xǐyīdiàn

laundry room 洗衣房 xǐyīfáng

lavatory 卫生间 wèishēngjiān

lavender (colour) 淡紫色 dànzǐsè

(plant) 薰衣草 xūnyīcǎo

law 法律 fǎlǜ

lawn 草坪 cǎopíng

lawyer 律师 lǜshī

laxative 泻药 xièyào

layby 路侧停车处 lùcè tíngchēchù

lazy 懒惰的 lǎnduò de

lead (dog) 皮带 pídài

(electrical) 导线 dǎoxiàn

lead (metal) 铅 qiān

lead-free 无铅的 wúqiān de

leaf 叶 yè

leak (of gas, liquid) 裂隙 lièxì

to leak (pipe, shoes etc) 漏 lòu

to learn about something 学到某物 xuédào mǒuwù

lease 租 zū

least: at least 至少 zhìshǎo

leather 皮革 pígé

(jacket, shoes etc) 皮制的 pízhìde

leave (bus, train) 出发 chūfā

(leave behind) 留下 liúxià

leek 韭葱 jiǔcōng

left (not right) 左 zuǒ

left-luggage 行李暂存 xínglì zàncún

left-luggage locker 行李寄存柜 xínglì jìcún guì

leg 腿 tuǐ

legal 合法的 hé fǎ de

lemon 柠檬 níngméng

lemonade 柠檬汁 níngméng zhī

to lend 把某物借给某人 bǎ mǒuwù jiègěi mǒurén

length 长度 chángdù

lens (of camera) 镜头 jìngtóu

(of glasses) 镜片 jìngpiàn

lesbian 女同性恋的 nǚ tóngxìngliàn de

less 更小的 gèngxiǎode

less than half 不到一半 bùdào yībàn

lesson 课 kè

let (allow) 允许某人做某事 yǔnxǔ mǒurén zuò mǒushì

(lease) 出租 chūzū

letter 信 xìn

(of alphabet) 字母 zìmǔ

letterbox 信箱 xìnxiāng

lettuce 生菜 shēngcài

level crossing 平交道口

píngjiāodàokǒu
library 图书馆 túshūguǎn
licence 许可证 xǔkězhèng
(driving) 驾驶证 jiàshǐzhèng
lid 盖 gài
lie (untruth) 说谎 shuōhuǎng
to lie down 躺下 tǎngxià
life 生命 shēngmìng
lifebelt 救生带 jiùshēngdài
lifeboat 救生船 jiùshēngchuán
lifeguard 救生员 jiùshēngyuán
life insurance 人寿保险 rénshòu
bǎoxiǎn
life jacket 救生衣 jiùshēngyī
lift (elevator) 电梯 diàntī
(in car) 让某人搭便车 ràng mǒurén
dā biànchē
light 灯 dēng
(colour) 淡的 dàn de
(for cigarette) 打火机 dǎhuǒjī
(not heavy) 轻的 qīng de
light bulb 灯泡 dēngpào
lighter 打火机 dǎhuǒjī
lighthouse 灯塔 dēngtǎ
lightning 闪电 shǎndiàn
like 像 xiàng
to like 喜欢 xǐhuan
I'd like... 我想··· wǒ xiǎng...
I don't like... 我不喜欢··· wǒ bù
xǐhuan...
I like coffee 我喜欢咖啡 wǒ
xǐhuan kāfēi
we'd like... 我们想··· wǒmen
xiǎng...
lily 百合花 bǎihéhuā
lime 酸橙 suānchéng
line (phone) 线路 xiànlù
(queue, row) 排 pái
linen (cloth) 亚麻布 yàmábù
(sheets, tablecloths) 亚麻制品 yàmá
zhìpǐn
lingerie 女内衣 nǚ nèiyī
lion 狮子 shīzi
lip 唇 chún

lip-read 唇读 chúndú
lipstick 口红 kǒuhóng
liqueur 烈酒 lièjiǔ
list 单子 dānzi
to listen to 留神听某人说话
liúshén tīng mǒurén shuōhuà
litre 升 shēng
litter 垃圾 lājī
little 小的 xiǎo de
a little... 一点··· yīdiǎn...
to live in 住在··· zhùzài...
I live in London 我住在伦敦··· wǒ
zhùzài Lúndūn...
liver 肝脏 gānzàng
living room 起居室 qǐjūshì
lizard 蜥蜴 xīyì
loaf (of bread) 一条(面包) yītiáo
(miànbāo)
lobster 龙虾 lóngxiā
local (council, newspaper etc) 当地的
dāngdì de
(residents) 本地的 běndì de
lock 锁 suǒ
to lock (door etc) 锁上 suǒ shàng
locker 小柜 xiǎoguì
locksmith 锁匠 suǒjiàng
log (diary) 日志 rìzhì
(from tree) 原木 yuánmù
lollipop 棒棒糖 bàngbàngtáng
London 伦敦 Lúndūn
Londoner 伦敦人 Lúndūnrén
long 长的 chángde
long-sighted 远视的 yuǎnshì de
to look after 照顾 zhàogù
to look at 看 kàn
to look for 找 zhǎo
loose 松动的 sōngdòng de
lorry 卡车 kǎchē
to lose 丢失 diūshī
I've lost my... 我丢失了我的··· wǒ
diūshīle wǒde...
lost property office 失物认领处
shīwù rènlǐngchù
lot: *a lot* (many) 许多 xǔduō

(much) 很多 hěnduō

lotion 洗液 xǐyè

lottery 彩票 cǎipiào

loud (noisy) 响亮的 xiǎngliàng de

(speak out) 大声地 dàshēng de

lounge (in airport) 等候室 děnghòushì

(in hotel) 休息室 xiūxishì

love 爱 ài

lovely 可爱的 kě ài de

low 矮的 ǎi de

low-fat 低脂肪的 dī zhīfáng de

luck 幸运 xìngyùn

lucky: to be lucky 走运 zǒuyùn

luggage 行李 xínglì

luggage trolley 行李手推车 xínglìshǒutuīchē

lump (on body) 肿块 zhǒngkuài

lunch 午饭 wǔfàn

lunch break 午休时间 wǔxiū shíjiān

lung 肺 fèi

luxury 奢华 shēhuá

M

machine 机器 jīqì

mad (angry) 恼怒的 nǎonù de

(insane) 精神失常的 jīngshén shīcháng de

Madam/Ms... 女士 nǚshì

magazine 杂志 zázhì

maggot 蛆 qū

magnet 磁铁 cítiě

magnifying glass 放大镜 fàngdàjìng

magpie 喜鹊 xǐquè

maid 女仆 nǚpú

maiden name 娘家姓 niángjiā xìng

mail 邮政 yóuzhèng

by mail 以邮寄方式 yǐ yóujì fāngshì

main 主要的 zhǔyào de

main course (of meal) 主菜 zhǔcài

main road 主干道 zhǔ gàndào

to make (cake, clothes) 做 zuò

(noise) 制造 zhìzào

make-up 化妆品 huàzhuāngpǐn

male 男的 nánde

man 男人 nánrén

to manage (cope) 应付 yìngfù

manager 经理 jīnglǐ

managing director 总经理 jīnglǐ

manual 手工的 shǒugōng de

(handbook) 手册 shǒu cè

many 许多的 xǔduō de

Mandarin (language) 普通话 pǔtōnghuà

map (of country) 地图 dìtú

marathon 马拉松长跑 mǎlāsōng chángpǎo

marble 大理石 dàlǐshí

March 三月 sānyuè

marina 小艇船坞 xiǎotǐng chuánwù

mark (stain) 污点 wūdiǎn

(tick) 记号 jìhao

marketplace 市场 shìchǎng

marmalade 橘子酱 júzi jiàng

married 结婚了 jiéhūn le

are you married? 你结婚了吗? nǐ jiéhūn le ma?

I'm married 我已经结婚了 wǒ yǐjīngjiéhūn le

marry (man, woman) 和 ··· 结婚 hé ... jiéhūn

marsh 沼泽 zhǎozé

mascara 睫毛膏 jiémáogāo

mashed potato 土豆泥 tǔdòuní

mast (nautical) 船桅 chuánwéi

(radio etc) 天线杆 tiānxiàn gān

masterpiece 杰作 jiézuò

match (game) 比赛 bǐsài

(for lighting fire) 火柴 huǒchái

material (cloth) 衣料 yīliào

(substance) 材料 cáiliào

matter (be important) 要紧 yàojǐn

as a matter of fact 事实上 shìshí shàng

it doesn't matter 没关系 méi guānxi

mattress 床垫 chuángdiàn

maximum 最高的 zuìgāo de

May 五月 wǔyuè

mayor 市长 shìzhǎng

me 我 wǒ

meadow 草地 cǎodì

meal 饭 fàn

mean 表示 … 意思 biǎoshì … yìsī

measles 麻疹 mázhěn

measure 测量 cèliáng

meat 肉 ròu
(dish, pie) 肉类 ròulèi

mechanic 机械工 jīxiègōng

medicine 药 yào

medieval 中世纪的 zhōngshìjì de

Mediterranean (climate, diet) 地中海地区的 Dìzhōnghǎi dìqū de

medium 中等的 zhōngděng de

meet 会面 huìmiàn

pleased to meet you! 幸会! xìnghuì!

meeting 会议 huìyì

meeting place 会场 huìchǎng

melon 瓜 guā

melt 融化 rónghuà

member 一员 yīyuán

membership card 会员卡 huìyuán kǎ

memory 记忆力 jìyìlì

mend 修理 xiūlǐ

menu 菜单 càidān

set menu 套餐 tàocān

message 留言 liúyán

metal 金属 jīnshǔ

meter 仪表 yíbiǎo

metro (underground) 地铁 dìtiě

metro station 地铁站 dìtiězhàn

microwave oven 微波炉 wēibōlú

midday 正午 zhèngwǔ

middle 中央 zhōngyāng

middle-aged 中年的 zhōngnián de

midnight 半夜 bànyè

at midnight 在午夜 zài wǔyè

mild (climate) 温暖的 wēnnuǎn de
(taste) 淡味的 dànwèi de

mile 英里 yīnglǐ

military police 军警 jūnjǐng

milk 牛奶 niúnǎi

milk chocolate 牛奶巧克力 niúnǎi qiǎokèlì

milkshake 奶昔 nǎixī

millennium 一千年 yīqiānnián

millimetre 毫米 háomǐ

million 一百万 yībǎiwàn

mince 肉末 ròumò

mind: do you mind? 你介意吗? nǐ jièyì ma?

I don't mind 我不介意 wǒ bù jièyì

mineral water 矿泉水 kuàngquánshuǐ

Ming porcelain 明瓷器 míngcíqì

minibar 客房内酒吧 kèfángnèi jiǔbā

minimum 最低的 zuìdī de

minister 部长 bùzhǎng

mint (plant) 薄荷 bòhe
(sweet) 薄荷糖 bòhe táng

minute 分钟 fēnzhōng

mirror 镜子 jìngzi

misbehave 行为无礼 xíngwéi wúlǐ

miscarriage 流产 liúchǎn

Miss... …小姐 …xiǎo jiě

to miss (train etc) 误了 wùle

missing 失踪的 shīzōng de

misty 有雾的 yǒuwù de

it's misty 有雾 yǒuwù

mistake 错误 cuòwù

misunderstanding 误会 wùhuì

mix 混合 hùnhé

mixer 搅拌器 jiǎobànqì

mobile number 手机号码 shǒujī hàomǎ

mobile phone 手机 shǒujī

modem 调制解调器 tiáozhì jiětiáo qì

modern 现代的 xiàndài de

moisturizer 保湿霜 bǎoshīshuāng

mole 痣 zhì

moment 片刻 piànkè

monastery 寺院 sìyuàn

Monday 星期一 xīngqīyī

money 钱 qián

I have no money 我没有钱 wǒ méiyǒu qián

money order 汇票 huìpiào

monkey 猴 hóu

month 月 yuè

monthly 每月 měiyuè

monument 纪念碑 jìniànbēi

moon 月球 yuèqiú

mop 拖把 tuōbǎ

moped 机动自行车 jīdòng zìxíngchē

more 更多的 gèngduōde

more than 20 大于20 dàyú èrshí

some more... 更多的 gèngduōde

morning 早晨 zǎochén

good morning! 早上好! zǎoshàng hǎo!

this morning 今天上午 jīntiān shàngwǔ

mosque 清真寺 qīngzhēnsì

mosquito 蚊 wén

mosquito net 蚊帐 wénzhàng

most 大部分的 dàbùfen de

most people 大多数人 dàduōshù rén

moth 蛾 é

mother 母亲 mǔqīn

mother-in-law (of man) 岳母 yuèmǔ

(of woman) 婆婆 pópo

motor 发动机 fādòngjī

motorbike 摩托车 mótuōchē

motorboat 摩托艇 mótuōtǐng

motorcycle 摩托车 mótuōchē

motorway 高速公路 gāosùgōnglù

mountain 山 shān

mountain bike 山地自行车 shāndì zìxíngchē

mountaineering 登山运动 dēngshān yùndòng

mouse 鼠 shǔ

moustache 胡子 hú zī

mouth 嘴 zuǐ

mouthwash 漱口剂 shùkǒujì

move 移动 yídōng

movie 电影 diànyǐng

Mr... ...先生 ...xiānsheng

Mrs... ...太太 ...tàitai

much 大量的 dàliàng de

there isn't much left 剩下的不多了 shèngxià de bùduō le

mud 泥 ní

muddy 沾满烂泥的 zhānmǎn lànní de

mugging 抢劫 qiǎngjié

mumps 腮腺炎 sāixiànyán

muscle 肌肉 jīròu

museum 博物馆 bówùguǎn

mushrooms 蘑菇 mógu

music 音乐 yīnyuè

musical 音乐的 yīnyuè de

musical production 歌剧 gējù

must 必须 bìxū

mustard 芥末 jièmo

mutton 羊肉 yángròu

my 我的 wǒde

N

nail (finger, toe) 指甲 zhǐjia

(metal) 钉子 dīngzi

nailfile 指甲锉 zhǐjia cuò

nail polish 指甲油 zhǐjia yóu

nail polish remover 洗甲水 xǐjiǎ shuǐ

name 名字 míngzì

my name is... 我的名字是... wǒde míngzì shì...

what is your name? 你叫什么名字? nǐ jiào shénme míngzì?

nanny 保姆 bǎomǔ
napkin 餐巾 cānjīn
nappy 尿布 niàobù
narrow 窄的 zhǎi de
national 国家的 guójiā de
nationality 国籍 guójí
national park 国家公园 guójiā gōngyuán
natural 正常的 zhèngcháng de
nature 自然界 zìránjiè
navy-blue 藏青色 zàngqīngsè
near 近的 jìn de
near to... 靠近… kàojìn...
necessary 必要的 bìyào de
neck 颈 jǐng
necklace 项链 xiàngliàn
nectarine 油桃 yóutáo
need: *I need...* 我需要… wǒ xūyào...
we need... 我们需要… wǒmen xūyào...
needle 针 zhēn
negative 不好的 bù hǎo de
neighbour 邻居 línjū
nephew 侄子 zhízi
nest 巢 cháo
net 网 wǎng
never 从未 cóngwèi
new 新的 xīnde
news 消息 xiāoxi
(radio, TV) 新闻 xīnwén
newsagent 报摊 bàotān
newspaper 报纸 bàozhǐ
New Year 新年 xīnnián
Happy New Year! 新年快乐! xīnniánkuàilè!
New Year's Eve 元旦前夜 yuándàn qiányè
New Zealand 新西兰 Xīnxīlán
next 下一个的 xiàyīgè de
next door 隔壁 gébì
next to 旁边的 pángbiānde
nice 好的 hǎo de
(person) 和蔼的 hé'ǎi de

niece (brother's daughter) 侄女 zhínǚ
(sister's daughter) 甥女 shēngnǚ
night 黑夜 hēiyè
at night 夜间 yèjiān
nightclub 夜总会 yèzǒnghuì
nightdress 睡衣 shuìyī
nine 九 jiǔ
nineteen 十九 shíjiǔ
nineteenth 第九 dìjiǔ
ninety 九十 jiǔshí
no 不 bù
no entry 不许进入 bùxǔ jìnrù
no photography 禁止拍照 jìnzhǐpāizhào
no smoking 不许抽烟 bùxǔ chōuyān
no swimming 禁止游泳 jìnzhǐyóuyǒng
no, thanks 不, 谢谢 bù, xièxie
nobody 没有人 méiyǒu rén
noise 噪音 zàoyīn
noisy 嘈杂的 cáozá de
non-alcoholic 不含酒精的 bù hán jiǔjīng de
Northern Ireland 北爱尔兰 Běi'ài'érlán
none 没有一个 méiyǒu yī gè
non-smoker 不吸烟的人 bù xīyān de rén
non-smoking 禁烟的 jìn yān de
north 北方 běifāng
nose 鼻子 bízi
not 不 bù
note (banknote) 纸币 zhǐbì
(message) 便条 biàntiáo
notepad 记事本 jìshìběn
nothing 什么也没有 shénme yě méiyǒu
notice 注意到 zhùyì dào
noticeboard 布告栏 bùgàolán
novel 小说 xiǎoshuō
November 十一月 shíyīyuè
now 现在 xiànzài

nowhere 无处 wúchù
nuclear 核能的 hénéng de
nudist beach 裸体 luǒtǐ
number 号码 hàomǎ
number plate 车号牌 chēhàopái
nurse 护士 hùshi
nursery 幼儿园 yòu'éryuán
nut 坚果 jiānguǒ
nutmeg 肉豆蔻 ròudòukòu

O

oak 橡树 xiàngshù
oar 桨 jiǎng
oats 麦片 màipiàn
obtain 获得 huòdé
obvious 明显的 míngxiǎn de
occasionally 偶尔地 ǒu'ěr de
occupation 职业 zhíyè
ocean 海洋 hǎiyáng
occupied 有人 yǒurén
October 十月 shíyuè
octopus 章鱼 zhāngyú
odd (number) 奇数的 jīshù de
of 的 de
a kilo of flour 一公斤面粉 yī
gōngjīn miànfěn
made of 由 ··· 制成 yóu ...
zhìchéng
off 关着的 guānzhe de
(cheese, meat, milk etc) 不新鲜的 bù
xīnxiān de
offer 给 gěi
office 办公室 bàngōngshì
often 经常 jīngcháng
how often do you wash the car?
你多久洗一次车? nǐ duōjiǔ xǐ yīcì
chē?
oil 油 yóu
oil filter 滤油器 lǜyóuqì
ointment 油膏 yóugāo
OK! 好! hǎo!
old (not young) 老（不年轻）lǎo
(bù niánqīng)
how old are you? 你多大年纪了?

nǐ duōdà niánjìle?
I'm ... years old 我 ··· 岁了 wǒ ...
suìle
old age pensioner 拿退休金的人
ná tuìxiūjīn de rén
olive 橄榄 gǎnlǎn
olive oil 橄榄油 gǎnlǎnyóu
omelette 煎蛋饼 jiāndànbǐng
on 在 ··· 上 zài ... shang
it's on the table/wall 它在桌上/
墙上 tā zài zhuōshang/qiángshang
once 一次 yīcì
at once 马上 mǎshàng
one 一 yī
one hundred 一百 yībǎi
one-way 单行的 dānxíng de
onions 洋葱 yángcōng
only 仅仅 jǐnjǐn
open 打开 dǎkāi
opera 歌剧 gējù
opera house 歌剧院 gējùyuàn
operator 接线员 jiēxiànyuán
opium pipe 鸦片烟斗
yāpiànyāndǒu
opposite 对面的 duìmiànde
optician 眼镜商 yǎnjìngshāng
or 还是 háishì
orange (colour) 橙色 chéngsè
(fruit) 橙子 chéngzi
orange juice 橙汁 chénzhī
freshly squeezed orange juice
鲜榨橙汁 xiānzhàchéngzhī
orchestra 管弦乐队 guǎnxián
yuèduì
order 命令 mìnglìng
(in restaurant) 点菜 diǎncài
organic 有机的 yǒujī de
organize 组织 zǔzhī
original 最初的 zuìchū de
ornament 装饰物 zhuāngshìwù
other 另外的 lìngwài de
not this one 其他的 qítā de
our 我们的 wǒmende
out 在外面 zài wàimiàn

out here/there 这儿/那儿 zhèr/nàr

the ball was out 球出界了 qiú chūjiè le

outdoor 户外的 hùwài de

outside 外面 wàimiàn

oven 烤箱 kǎoxiāng

ovenproof 耐热的 nàirè de

oven-ready 即可入炉烤制的 jíkě rùlú kǎozhì de

over 结束的 jiéshù de

(on top of) 在 … 上 zài … shang

overbooked 超员预订的 chāoyuán yùdìng de

overcharge 要价太高 yàojià tàigāo

overcoat 大衣 dàyī

overdone 煮得过久的 zhǔde guòjiǔ de

overdose 过量用药 guòliàng yòngyào

overheat 变得过热 biànde guòrè

overload 使超载 shǐ chāozài

oversleep 睡过头 shuì guòtóu

overtake 超过 chāoguò

owe: *I owe you…* 我欠你… wǒ qiàn nǐ…

you owe me… 你欠我… nǐ qiàn wǒ…

owl 猫头鹰 māotóuyīng

owner 物主 wùzhǔ

oxygen 氧气 yǎngqì

oyster 牡蛎 mǔlì

P

pace 速度 sùdù

pacemaker 起搏器 qǐbóqì

pack (bag, suitcase) 把 … 装箱 bǎ … zhuāngxiāng

package 包裹 bāoguǒ

package holiday 包价旅游 bāojià lǚyóu

packet 盒 hé

padding 填塞物 tiánsāiwù

paddling pool 浅水池 qiǎnshuǐchí

padlock 挂锁 guàsuǒ

page 页 yè

paid 有薪金的 yǒu xīnjīn de

pain 疼痛 téngtòng

painful 疼痛的 téngtòng de

painkiller 止痛药 zhǐtòngyào

paint 油漆 yóuqī

painting (picture) 画 huà

pair 双/对 shuāng/duì

palace 宫殿 gōngdiàn

pale 灰暗的 huī'àn de

pan 炖锅 dùnguō

pancake 薄煎饼 báojiānbing

pant 喘气 chuǎnqì

paper 纸 zhǐ

paper hanky 面巾纸 miànjīnzhǐ

paracetamol 扑热息痛 pūrèxītòng

parcel 包裹 bāoguǒ

pardon? 您说什么? nín shuō shénme?

I beg your pardon? 请您再说一遍? qǐng nín zài shuō yībiàn?

parents 父母 fùmǔ

park 公园 gōngyuán

to park 停车 tíngchē

parking meter 停车计时器 tíngchē jìshíqì

parking ticket 违章停车罚款单 wéizhāng tíngchē fákuǎndān

part 部分 bùfen

partner (boyfriend/girlfriend) 伴侣 bànlǚ

(business) 伙伴 huǒbàn

party (celebration) 晚会 wǎnhuì

(political) 党 dǎng

pass 度过 dùguò

(overtake) 超过 chāoguò

passenger 旅客 lǚkè

passport 护照 hùzhào

passport control 验照处 yànzhàochù

pasta 意大利面条 yìdàlì miàntiáo

pastry (cake) 糕点 gāodiǎn

by post 以邮件的方式 yǐ yóujì de fāngshì
postbox 邮箱 yóuxiāng
postcard 明信片 míngxìnpiàn
postcode 邮政编码 yóuzhèngbiānmǎ
poster 海报 hǎibào
post office 邮电局 yóudiànjú
postman/postwoman 邮递员/女邮递员 yóudìyuán/nǚ yóudìyuán
postpone 推迟 tuīchí
pot (cooking) 锅 guō
potato 土豆 tǔdòu
potato chips 薯片 shǔpiàn
potato peeler 马铃薯削皮器 mǎlíngshǔ xiāopíqì
pottery 陶器 táoqì
pound (money) 镑 bàng
(weight) 磅 bàng
to pour 灌某物 guàn mǒuwù
powder 粉 fěn
powdered milk 奶粉 nǎifěn
power 权力 quánlì
power cut 停电 tíngdiàn
pram 婴儿车 yīng'érchē
prawn 虾 xiā
pray 祷告 dǎogào
prayer 祷告人 dǎogào rén
prefer 偏爱 piān'ài
pregnant 怀孕的 huáiyùn de
prepare 准备 zhǔnbèi
prescribe 开 kāi
prescription 处方 chǔfāng
present (gift) 礼物 lǐwù
preservative 防腐剂 fángfǔjì
price 价格 jiàgé
price list 价目表 jiàmùbiǎo
priest 神职人员 shénzhí rényuán
prince 王子 wángzǐ
princess 公主 gōngzhǔ
print (photograph) 照片 zhàopiàn
(type) 印刷字体 yìnshuā zìtǐ
printer (machine) 打印机 dǎyìnjī

(person) 印刷工 yìnshuā gōng
prison 监狱 jiānyù
private facilities 私人设施 sīrénshèshī
prize 奖 jiǎng
probably 可能 kěnéng
problem 问题 wèntí
no problem! 没问题！méi wèntí!
professor 教授 jiàoshòu
programme (radio, TV) 节目 jiémù
promise 许诺 xǔnuò
to pronounce 发音 fāyīn
protein 蛋白质 dànbáizhì
Protestant 新教徒 Xīnjiàotú
provide 供应 gōngyìng
public 公众的 gōngzhòng de
public holiday 公共假期 gōnggòng jiàqī
publisher 出版商 chūbǎnshāng
pudding 布丁 bùdīng
to pull 拉 lā
pullover 套头衫 tàotóushān
pump 泵 bèng
pumpkin 南瓜 nánguā
puncture 刺孔 cìkǒng
puppet 木偶 mù'ǒu
puppy 小狗 xiǎogǒu
purple 紫色的 zǐsè de
purpose 目的 mùdì
on purpose 故意地 gùyì de
purse 钱包 qiánbāo
to push 推 tuī
pushchair 幼儿车 yòu'érchē
put 放 fàng
put back 放回 fànghuí
pyjamas 睡衣 shuìyī

Q

quail 鹌鹑 ānchún
quality 质量 zhìliàng
quantity 数量 shùliàng
quarantine 检疫 jiǎnyì
to quarrel 争吵 zhēngchǎo
quarter 四分之一 sìfēnzhīyī

quay 码头 mǎtóu
queen 女王 nǚwáng
query 疑问 yíwèn
question 问题 wèntí
queue 排队 páiduì
to queue 为 … 排队 wèi … páiduì
quick 快的 kuài de
quickly 很快地 hěnkuài de
quiet (place) 安静 ānjìng
be quiet! 请安静! qǐng ānjìng!
quilt 被子 bèizi
quite 相当 xiāngdāng
quite a few 相当多 xiāngdāng duō
I can't quite remember
我不太记得了 wǒ bùtài jìdé le
quiz 测验 cèyàn

R

rabbit 兔子 tùzi
rabies 狂犬病 kuángquǎnbìng
race (ethnic group) 种族 zhǒngzú
(sport) 赛跑 sàipǎo
racecourse 赛马场 sàimǎchǎng
rack (luggage) 行李架 xínglijià
racket (tennis etc) 球拍 qiúpāi
radiator (in car) 散热器 sànrèqì
(on wall) 暖气片 nuǎnqìpiàn
radio 收音机 shōuyīnjī
radish 萝卜 luóbo
raffle tickets 摸奖游戏 mō jiǎng
yóuxì
railway 铁路 tiělù
railway station 火车站
huǒchēzhàn
rain 雨 yǔ
it's raining 正在下雨 zhèngzài
xiàyǔ
to rain 下雨 xiàyǔ
rainbow 彩虹 cǎihóng
raincoat 雨衣 yǔyī
raisin 葡萄干 pútáogān
rake 耙 pá
rape 强奸 qiángjiān
raped 被强奸 bèiqiángjiān

rare (steak) 半熟的 bànshóu de
(uncommon) 稀有的 xīyǒu de
rash (skin) 皮疹 pízhěn
raspberry 山莓 shānméi
rat 田鼠 tiánshǔ
rate (price) 费用 fèiyòng
rate of exchange 兑换率
duìhuànlǜ
raw 生的 shēng de
razor 剃须刀 tìxūdāo
razor blade 剃须刀刀片 tìxūdāo
dāopiàn
read 阅读 yuèdú
ready 做好准备的 zuòhǎo
zhǔnbèi de
real 真正的 zhēnzhèng de
realize 意识到 yìshìdào
rear-view mirror 后视镜
hòushìjìng
reason 原因 yuányīn
receipt 收据 shōujù
receiver 听筒 tīngtǒng
recently 最近 zuìjìn
reception (desk) 接待处 jiēdàichù
receptionist 接待员 jiēdàiyuán
recharge 充电 chōngdiàn
recipe 食谱 shípǔ
recognize 认出 rènchū
recommend 推荐 tuījiàn
record (music) 唱片 chàngpiàn
(written account) 记载 jìzǎi
recover 恢复 huīfù
recycle 再生利用 zàishēng lìyòng
red 红色的 hóngsède
reduce 减少 jiǎnshǎo
reduction 折扣 zhékòu
refund 退款 tuìkuǎn
reel (fishing) 绕线轮 ràoxiànlún
refer 叫某人看看 jiào mǒurén
cānkàn
referee 裁判员 cáipànyuán
refill 再装满 zàizhuāngmǎn
refund 退款 tuìkuǎn
refuse 拒绝 jùjué

regarding 关于 guānyú
region 区域 qūyù
register 注册 zhùcè
registration form 注册表格 zhùcèbiǎogé
regulation 规章 guīzhāng
reimburse 偿还 chánghuán
relation 亲戚 qīnqi
relationship 关系 guānxi
relative 亲戚 qīnqi
relax 放松 fàngsōng
reliable 可靠的 kěkào de
remain 仍然是 réngrán shì
remember 记住 jìzhù
remote control 遥控 yáokòng
removal 去除 qùchú
remove 移走 yízǒu
rent (car, land, room) 租用 zūyòng
rent out (house, room) 出租 chūzū
rental 租金 zūjīn
repair 修理 xiūlǐ
repeat 重复 chóngfù
reply 回答 huídá
report 报告 bàogào
request 要求 yāoqiú
require 需要 xūyào
rescue 营救 yíngjiù
reservation 预定 yùdìng
to reserve 预定 yùdìng
reserved 已预定的 yǐ yùdìng de
resident 居民 jūmín
resort 度假胜地 dùjià shèngdì
rest (remainder) 剩余 shèngyú
(repose) 休息 xiūxi
to rest 休息 xiūxi
restaurant 餐馆 cānguǎn
restaurant car 餐车 cānchē
retired: I'm retired 我退休了 wǒ tuìxiū le
(go to bed) 就寝 jiùqǐn
return 返回 fǎnhuí
return ticket 往返票 wǎngfǎnpiào
reverse 相反 xiāngfǎn
reverse gear 倒车档 dàochēdǎng

reverse-charge call 受话人付费电话 shòuhuàrén fùfèi diànhuà
rheumatism 风湿病 fēngshībìng
rib 肋骨 lèigǔ
ribbon 饰带 shìdài
rice 大米 dàmǐ
rich (country, person) 富有的 fùyǒu de
(food) 油腻的 yóunì de
ride (bicycle, car) 兜风 dōufēng
(bus, horse, train) 出行 chūxíng
right (correct) 正确的 zhèngquè de
(not left) 右 yòu
right-handed 惯用右手的 guànyòng yòushǒu de
right of way 通行权 tōngxíngquán
ring (bell) 使 ··· 响 shǐ … xiǎng
(finger) 戒指 jièzhi
(telephone) 响 xiǎng
ring road 环路 huánlù
ripe 成熟的 chéngshú de
river 河 hé
road 公路 gōnglù
road map 公路地图 gōnglù dìtú
road sign 路标 lùbiāo
roadworks 道路施工 dàolù shīgōng
roast 烤 kǎo
robber 强盗 qiángdào
robin 知更鸟 zhīgēngniǎo
roll (bread) 小圆面包 xiǎoyuánmiànbāo
rollerblades 直排轮溜冰鞋 zhípáilún liūbīngxié
rolling pin 擀面杖 gǎnmiànzhàng
romance 浪漫 làngmàn
romantic 浪漫的 làngmàn de
roof 屋顶 wūdǐng
roof rack 车顶架 chēdǐng jià
room (hotel) 客房 kèfáng
double room 双人房 shuāngrénfáng

single room 单人房 dānrénfáng

room service 客房送餐服务
kèfáng sòngcān fúwù

root 根 gēn

rope 绳子 shéngzi

rose 玫瑰 méiguì

rosé wine 玫瑰红葡萄酒
méiguìhóng pútáojiǔ

rotten 腐烂的 fǔlàn de

rough (sea) 波涛汹涌的 bōtāo
xiōngyǒng de

(surface) 粗糙的 cūcāo de

round 圆的 yuán de

roundabout 环形交叉路
huánxíng jiāochālù

route 路 lù

row 一排 yī pái

rowing 赛艇运动 sàitǐng yùndòng

rowing boat 划艇 huátǐng

royal 皇家的 huángjiā de

rubber (substance) 橡胶 xiàngjiāo

rubber band 橡皮筋 xiàngpíjīn

rubbish 垃圾 lājī

rudder 舵 duò

rug 小地毯 xiǎodìtǎn

ruin 毁坏 huǐhuài

ruler (measuring) 直尺 zhíchǐ

rum 朗姆酒 lǎngmǔjiǔ

run 跑步 pǎobù

rush 匆忙 cōngmáng

rusty 生锈的 shēngxiù de

S

saccharin 糖精 tángjīng

sad 伤心的 shāngxīn de

saddle (bike) 车座 chēzuò

(horse) 马鞍 mǎ'ān

safe (medicine etc) 安全的
ānquánde

(for valuables) 保险柜 bǎoxiǎnguì

safety 安全 ānquán

safety pin 安全别针 ānquán
biézhēn

sage 鼠尾草 shǔwěicǎo

sail 帆 fān

sailboat 帆船 fānchuán

sailing 帆船运动 fānchuán
yùndòng

saint 圣徒 shèngtú

salad 凉拌菜 liángbàncài

salad dressing 凉拌菜调味料
liángbàncài tiáowèiliào

salary 薪水 xīnshuǐ

sale 廉售 liánshòu

salesman/woman 销售员
xiāoshòuyuán

sales rep 推销员 tuīxiāo yuán

salmon 大马哈鱼 dà mǎhā yú

salt 盐 yán

saltwater 咸水的 xiánshuǐ de

salty 咸的 xián de

same 相同的 xiāngtóng de

sample 样品 yàngpǐn

sand 沙 shā

sandal 凉鞋 liángxié

sandwich 三明治 sānmíngzhì

sanitary towel 卫生巾 wèishēng
jīn

sardine 沙丁鱼 shādīng yú

satellite (communications)
人造卫星 rénzào wèixīng

satellite TV 卫星电视 wèixīng
diànshì

Saturday 星期六 xīngqīliù

sauce 酱 jiàng

saucepan 深平底锅 shēn píngdǐ
guō

saucer 茶杯碟 chábēi dié

sauna 桑拿浴 sāngná yù

sausage 香肠 xiāngcháng

save (money) 积攒 jīzǎn

(person) 救 jiù

savouries 小吃 xiǎochī

saw 锯 jù

say 说 shuō

scale 规模 guīmó

scallop 扇贝 shànbèi

scan 仔细察看 zǐxì chákàn

scanner 扫描器 sǎomiáoqì

scarf 围巾 wéijīn

scenery 风景 fēngjǐng

schedule 日程安排 rìchéng ānpái

school 学校 xuéxiào

scissors 剪刀 jiǎndāo

score 比分 bǐfēn

Scotland 苏格兰 Sūgélán

Scottish 苏格兰人 Sūgélánrén

screen 银幕 yínmù

screw 螺丝 luósī

screwdriver 螺丝起子 luósīqǐzi

sea 大海 dàhǎi

seafood 海鲜 hǎixiān

seagull 海鸥 hǎi'ōu

seal 海豹 hǎibào

seam 缝 fèng

search 搜寻 sōuxún

seasick 晕船的 yūnchuán de

seaside: *at the seaside* 在海边 zàihǎibiān

season (of year) 季节 jìjié

season ticket 季票 jìpiào

seat (chair) 座位 zuòwèi

seatbelt 安全带 ānquándài

seaweed 海草 hǎicǎo

second 第二 dì'èr

second-class 二等的 èrděng de

second-hand 二手的 èrshǒu de

secretary 秘书 mìshū

security guard 保安人员 bǎo'ān rényuán

sedative 镇静剂 zhènjìng jì

to see 看 kàn

see you later 一会儿见 yī huìr jiàn

see you tomorrow 明天见 míng tiān jiàn

seed 种子 zhǒngzi

seize 抓住 zhuāzhù

self-catering 自供伙食的 zìgōng huǒshí de

self-service 自助的 zìzhù de

to sell 卖 mài

do you sell...? 你们卖 … 吗?

nǐmen mài ... ma?

sell-by date
商品必须售出的截止日期
shāngpǐn bìxū shòuchū de jiézhǐ rìqī

Sellotape® 透明胶带 tòumíng jiāodài

semi-skimmed (milk) 半脱脂奶 bàn tuōzhīnǎi

send 将某物发送 jiāng mǒuwù fāsòng

senior citizen
已届退休年龄的公民 yǐjiè tuìxiū niánlíng de gōngmín

sensible 通情达理的 tōngqíng dálǐ de

separated 分居的 fēnjū de

separately 分开地 fēnkāi de

September 九月 jiǔyuè

sequel (film, story) 续集 xùjí

series/soap (TV) 连续剧 liánxùjù

serious 严重的 yánzhòng de

serve 供职于 gòngzhíyú

service 服务 fúwù

service charge 服务费 fúwùfèi

service station 加油站 jiāyóu zhàn

serviette 餐巾 cānjīn

set menu 套餐菜单 tàocān càidān

settee 长沙发椅 cháng shāfāyǐ

seven 七 qī

seventeen 十七 shíqī

seventh 第七 dìqī

seventy 七十 qīshí

several 几个 jǐgè

sew 缝 féng

sewer 排污管 páiwū guǎn

sex (gender) 性别 xìngbié

shade 阴凉处 yīnliáng chù

shake 猛摇 měngyáo

shallow 浅的 qiǎn de

shampoo 洗发液 xǐfàyè

share 一份 yífèn

to share out 平均分配 píngjūn fēnpèi

sharp 锋利的 fēnglì de

shave 剃毛发 tìmáofà

shaving cream 剃须膏 tìxūgāo

shawl 披肩 pījiān

she 她 tā

sheep 绵羊 miányáng

sheet (bed) 床单 chuángdān

shelf 架子 jiàzi

shell 贝壳 bèiké

shellfish 贝类海产 bèilèi hǎichǎn

sheltered 遮风避雨的 zhēfēng bìyǔ de

shepherd 牧羊人 mùyángrén

sherry 雪利酒 xuělìjiǔ

shine 照耀 zhàoyào

ship 船 chuán

shirt 衬衫 chènshān

shoe 鞋 xié

shoelace 鞋带 xiédài

shoe polish 鞋油 xiéyóu

shoe shop 鞋店 xiédiàn

shop 商店 shāngdiàn

shop assistant 店员 diànyuán

shop window 商店橱窗 shāngdiàn chúchuāng

shore 岸 àn

shortage 短缺 duǎnquē

short-circuit 发生短路 fāshēng duǎnlù

short cut 近路 jìnlù

shorts 短裤 duǎnkù

short-sighted 近视的 jìnshì de

shoulder 肩膀 jiānbǎng

shout 喊叫声 hǎnjiào

show 表示 biǎoshì

shower 阵雨 zhènyǔ

shower cap 浴帽 yùmào

shower gel 沐浴露 mùyùlù

shrimp 小虾 xiǎoxiā

shrink 缩水 suōshuǐ

shrub 灌木 guànmù

shut 关上 guānshang

shutter 百叶窗 bǎiyèchuāng

shuttle 穿梭班机/班车 chuānsuō bānjī/bānchē

shy 害羞的 hàixiū de

sick 患病的 huànbìng de

side 边 biān

sidelight 侧灯灯 cèdēng

sidewalk 人行道 rénxíngdào

sieve 筛子 shāizi

sightseeing tour 观光游览 guānguāngyóulǎn

sign 指示牌 zhǐshìpái

signature 签名 qiānmíng

signpost 路标 lùbiāo

silk 丝绸 sīchóu

silk dress 真丝连衣裙 zhēnsīliányīqún

silk scarf 丝巾 sījīn

silk tie 真丝领带 zhēnsīlǐngdài

silver 银 yín

similar 相似的 xiāngsì de

simple 简单的 jiǎndān de

since 此后 cǐhòu

sing 唱歌 chànggē

single (unmarried) 单身的 dānshēnde

single bed 单人床 dānrénchuáng

single room 单人房 dānrénfáng

sink 洗涤槽 xǐdícáo

Sir 先生 xiānshēng

sister 姐妹 jiěmèi

sister-in-law (husband's sister) 姑子 gūzi

(wife's sister) 姨子 yízi

to sit 坐下 zuòxià

please, sit down 请坐下 qǐngzuòxià

six 六 liù

sixteen 十六 shíliù

sixth 第六 dìliù

sixty 六十 liùshí

size 大小 dàxiǎo

ski pass 滑雪通票 huáxuětōngpiào

skimmed milk 脱脂牛奶 tuōzhī niúnǎi

skin 皮肤 pífū

skirt 短裙 duǎnqún

skis 雪橇 xuěqiāo

sky 天 tiān

slang 俚语 lǐyǔ

sledge 雪橇 xuěqiāo

to sleep 睡觉 shuìjiào

sleeper (train) 卧车 wòchē

sleeping bag 睡袋 shuìdài

sleeping car 火车卧铺车厢 huǒchē wòpù chēxiāng

sleeping pill 安眠药 ānmiányào

slice 片 piàn

slide (photograph) 幻灯片 huàndēngpiàn

to slip something into 将某物悄悄塞入某物 jiāng mǒuwù qiāoqiāo sāirù mǒuwù

slipper 拖鞋 tuōxié

slow 慢的 màn de

small 小 xiǎo

smaller 小些 xiǎoxiē

smell 气味 qìwèi

smile 微笑 wēixiào

smoke: *to smoke/smoking* 抽烟 chōuyān

I don't smoke 我不抽烟 wǒ bù chōuyān

may I smoke? 我能抽烟吗? wǒ néng chōuyān ma?

smoke alarm 烟雾报警器 yānwù bàojǐngqì

smoked 熏制的 xūnzhì de

smoker 吸烟者 xīyānzhě

smooth 光滑的 guānghuá de

snack 小吃 xiǎochī

snack bar 小吃部 xiǎochībù

snake 蛇 shé

sneeze 打喷嚏 dǎ pēntì

snore 打鼾 dǎhān

snorkel 潜水通气管 qiánshuǐ tōngqìguǎn

snow 雪 xuě

to snow: *it's snowing* 正在下雪 zhèngzài xiàxuě

snowboard 滑雪板 huáxuěbǎn

so 这样 zhèyàng

if so 如果这样 rúguǒ zhèyàng

so far 迄今为止 qìjīn wéizhǐ

soap 肥皂 féizào

soap powder 洗衣粉 xǐyīfěn

sober 清醒的 qīng xǐng de

socket 插座 chāzuò

socks 短袜 duǎnwà

soda water 苏打水 sūdá shuǐ

sofa 沙发 shāfā

sofa bed 沙发床 shāfā chuáng

soft 松软的 sōngruǎn de

soft drink 软饮料 ruǎnyǐnliào

software 软件 ruǎnjiàn

soldier 士兵 shìbīng

soluble 可溶的 kěróng de

some 一些 yīxiē

someone 某人 mǒurén

something 某事物 mǒushìwù

sometimes 有时 yǒushí

son 儿子 érzi

son-in-law 女婿 nǚxu

song 歌 gē

soon 不久 bùjiǔ

see you soon! 再见! zàijiàn!

sore 痛的 tòng de

sore throat 喉咙疼 hōulóngténg

sort 种类 zhǒnglèi

all sorts of 各种不同的 gèzhǒng bùtóng de

sorry: *I'm sorry!* 对不起! duìbuqǐ!

sound (noise) 声音 shēngyīn

soup 汤 tāng

sour 酸的 suān de

south 南方 nánfāng

souvenir 礼品 lǐpǐn

soya sauce 酱油 jiàngyóu

spa (health) 美容健身院 měiróng jiànshēn yuàn

space (gap) 空隙 kòngxì

Spain 西班牙 Xībānyá

Spanish (language) 西班牙语 Xībānyáyǔ

(people) 西班牙人 Xībānyárén

spare part 备件 bèijiàn

spare time 业余时间 yèyú shíjiān

spark plug 火花塞 huǒhuāsāi

sparkle 光亮 guāngliàng

sparkling water 苏打水 sūdáshuǐ

sparkling wine 汽酒 qìjiǔ

to speak 说 shuō

do you speak English? 你说英文吗? nǐ shuō yīngwén ma?

I don't speak Mandarin 我不会说普通话 wǒ bù huì shuō pǔtōnghuà

special 特别的 tèbié de

specialist 一位 … 方面的专家 yīwèi … fāngmiàn de zhuānjiā

speciality 特制品 tèzhìpǐn

speech 演说 yǎnshuō

speed 速度 sùdù

speedboat 快艇 kuàitǐng

speed limit 速度限制 sùdù xiànzhì

speeding 超速 chāosù

spell 拼写 pīnxiě

he can't spell 他不会拼写 tā bùhuì pīnxiě

spend 花费 huāfèi

spice 香料 xiāngliào

spicy 辛辣的 xīnlà de

spider 蜘蛛 zhīzhū

spill 使溢出 shǐ yìchū

spin-dry 甩干 shuǎigān

spine 脊柱 jǐzhù

spinach 菠菜 bōcài

spirits (alcohol) 酒 jiǔ

spoon 勺子 sháozi

sport 运动 yùndòng

sports shop 体育用品商店 tǐyùyòngpǐn shāngdiàn

spot (mark) 斑点 bāndiǎn

(pimple) 疵点 cīdiǎn

spring (season) 春天 chūntiān

(wire coil) 弹簧 tánhuáng

spring onion 小葱 xiǎocōng

square (in town) 广场 guǎngchǎng

squash (drink) 浓缩橙汁, 需加水再喝 nóngsuō chéngzhī, xū jiāshuǐ zài hē

(vegetable) 南瓜 nánguā

squeeze 紧握 jǐnwò

squid 鱿鱼 yóuyú

stadium 体育场 tǐyùchǎng

staff 员工 yuángōng

stage 舞台 wǔtái

stain 污迹 wūjì

stained glass 彩色玻璃 cǎisè bōli

stair 梯级 tījí

stale 陈的 chén de

stalls (theatre) 正厅前排 zhèngtīngqiánpái

stamp 邮票 yóupiào

stand 摊子 tānzi

star 星 xīng

start 开始 kāishǐ

starter (food) 开胃菜 kāiwèi cài

station 车站 chēzhàn

bus station 公共汽车站 gōnggòngqìchēzhàn

railway station 火车站 huǒchēzhàn

underground station 地铁站 dìtiězhàn

statue 塑像 sùxiàng

to stay (remain) 住 zhù

I'm staying at... 我住在… wǒ zhùzài...

steak 牛排 niúpái

to steal 偷 tōu

steam 蒸汽 zhēngqì

steel 钢铁 gāngtiě

steep 陡的 dǒu de

steeple 尖塔 jiāntǎ

steering 转向 zhuǎnxiàng

steering wheel 方向盘 fāngxiàngpán

step (stair) 阶梯 jiē tī

stepbrother (same father) 异母兄弟 yìmǔ xiōngdì

(same mother) 异父兄弟 yìfù xiōngdì

stepdaughter 继女 jìnǚ

stepfather 继父 jìfù

stepmother 继母 jìmǔ

stereo 立体声装置 lìtǐ shēng zhuāngzhì

sterling (currency) 英国货币 yīngguó huòbì

stew 炖的食物 dùn de shíwù

steward 乘务员 chéngwù yuán

stewardess 女乘务员 nǚ chéngwù yuán

stick 枯枝 kūzhī

still 不动的 bùdòng de

sting 刺 cì

stitch 针脚 zhēnjiǎo

stock 供应物 gōngyìng wù

stocking 长统袜 chángtǒng wà

stole 披肩 pījiān

stomach 胃 wèi

stomach ache 胃疼 wèiténg

stone 石头 shítou

to stop (come to a halt) 停止 tíngzhǐ

store 商场 shāngchǎng

storey 层 céng

storm 暴风雨 bàofēngyǔ

story 故事 gùshi

straight 笔直的 bǐzhí de

straight on 一直往前走 yīzhí wǎngqiánzǒu

strange 奇怪的 qíguài de

straw 稻草 dàocǎo

strawberries 草莓 cǎoméi

stream 溪流 xīliú

street 街道 jiēdào

street map 街道地图 jiēdào dìtú

strength 力气 lìqi

stress 压力 yālì

strike 罢工 bàgōng

string 细绳 xìshéng

striped 有条纹的 yǒu tiáowén de

stroke (medical) 中风 zhòngfēng

strong 有力的 yǒulì de

(taste) 浓重的 nóng zhòng de

stuck 卡住 qiǎzhù

student 学生 xuéshēng

stupid 笨的 bèn de

subscription 订阅 dìngyuè

subtitles 字幕 zìmù

subway 地铁 dìtiě

suddenly 突然 tūrán

sugar 糖 táng

suggest 建议 jiànyì

suit 西装 xīzhuāng

suitcase 手提箱 shǒutíxiāng

sum 数额 shù'é

summer 夏天 xiàtiān

summertime 夏季 xiàjì

summit 峰顶 fēngdǐng

sun 太阳 tàiyáng

to sunbathe 日光浴 rìguāngyù

sunblock 防晒油 fángshàiyóu

sunburn 晒伤 shài shāng

Sunday 星期日 xīngqīrì

sunflower 向日葵 xiàngrìkuí

sunny 晴朗的 qínglǎng de

sunglasses 太阳镜 tàiyángjìng

sunrise 拂晓 fúxiǎo

sun roof 遮阳篷顶 zhēyáng péngdǐng

sunscreen 遮光屏 zhēguāng píng

sunset 傍晚 bàngwǎn

sunshine 阳光 yángguāng

suntan 晒黑 shàihēi

(cream, lotion) 防晒 fángshài

supermarket 超市 chāoshì

supper (dinner) 晚餐 wǎncān

supplement 补充 bǔchōng

supply 提供 tígōng

surcharge 附加费 fùjiā fèi

sure 有把握的 yǒu bǎwò de

surf 拍岸的浪花 pāi'àn de lànghuā

(Internet) 上网 shàng wǎng

surfboard 冲浪板 chōnglàng bǎn
surgery 外科手术 wàikē shǒushù
surname 姓 xìng
my surname is... 我姓··· wǒxìng...
surprise 意想不到的事物 yìxiǎng bùdào de shìwù
surrounding 周围的 zhōuwéi de
suspension 暂令停职 zànlìng tíngzhí
to swallow 吞咽 tūnyàn
swan 天鹅 tiāné
swear 咒骂 zhòumà
sweat 汗水 hànshuǐ
sweater 毛衣 máoyī
sweatshirt 棉毛衫 miánmáoshān
sweet (chocolate, mint) 糖果 tángguǒ
(dessert) 甜点 tiándiǎn
sweetener 代糖 dàitáng
swell (injury) 肿胀 zhǒngzhàng
swim 游水 yóushuǐ
swimming pool 游泳池 yóuyǒngchí
swimsuit 游泳衣 yóuyǒngyī
swing 秋千 qiūqiān
Swiss (language) 瑞士语 Ruìshìyǔ
(people) 瑞士人 Ruìshìrén
to switch off/on 关/开 guān/kāi
Switzerland 瑞士 Ruìshì
swollen 肿胀的 zhǒngzhàng de
swordfish 箭鱼 jiànyú
syringe 注射器 zhùshè qì

T

t-shirt T恤衫 Txùshān
table 桌子 zhuōzi
tablecloth 桌布 zhuōbù
tablespoon 餐匙 cānchí
table tennis 乒乓球 pīngpāngqiú
tablet (pill) 药片 yàopiàn
tail 尾巴 wěiba
tailor 裁缝 cáifeng
take (bath, shower) 洗 xǐ
(holiday) 度 dù
take (steal) 偷走 tōuzǒu

takeaway 外卖店 wàimàidiàn
takeoff 起飞 qǐfēi
talc 爽身粉 shuǎngshēnfěn
talk 讲话 jiǎnghuà
tall 高的 gāo de
tame 驯服的 xùnfú de
tampon 月经棉栓 yuèjīng miánshuān
Tang poetry 唐诗 tángshī
tangerine 红橘 hóngjú
tank 坦克 tǎnkè
(fish) 缸 gāng
tap 龙头 lóngtóu
tape (cassette) 磁带 cídài
tape measure 卷尺 juǎnchǐ
tape recorder 录音机 lùyīnjī
target 目标 mùbiāo
taste 味觉 wèijué
tax 税 shuì
taxi 出租车 chūzūchē
taxi driver 出租司机 chūzū sījī
taxi rank 出租车候客站 chūzūchē hòukèzhàn
tea 茶 chá
Chinese green tea 中国绿茶 zhōngguólǜchá
green tea 绿茶 lǜchá
red tea 红茶 hóng chá
tea bag 袋茶 dàichá
teach: *to teach somebody something* 教某人某事 jiāo mǒurén mǒushì
teacher 教师 jiàoshī
team 组 zǔ
tear (crying) 眼泪 yǎnlèi
(hole, rip) 裂口 lièkǒu
teaspoon 茶匙 cháchí
tea towel 擦拭布 cāshìbù
teenager 青少年 qīngshàonián
teeth 牙 yá
telephone 电话 diànhuà
to telephone 打电话 dǎ diànhuà
telephone box 电话亭 diànhuàtíng

telephone card 电话卡 diànhuàkǎ

telephone number 电话号码 diànhuà hàomǎ

television 电视 diànshì

to tell 告诉 gàosù

temperature 温度 wēndù

to have a temperature 发烧 fāshāo

temple 庙宇 miàoyǔ

temporary 临时的 línshí de

ten 十 shí

tenant 房客 fángkè

tenth 第十 dìshí

tennis 网球 wǎngqiú

tennis ball 网球 wǎngqiú

tennis court 网球场 wǎngqiúchǎng

tent 帐篷 zhàngpeng

tent peg 帐篷桩 zhàngpeng zhuāng

terminal 候机楼 hòu jī lǒu

terrace 成排的房屋 chéngpái de fángwū

terracotta 兵马俑 bīngmǎyǒng

terrorist 恐怖分子 kǒngbù fènzǐ

test 试验 shìyàn

tetanus 破伤风 pòshāngfēng

than 比 bǐ

more than 20 多于20 duōyú èrshí

thank you 谢谢您 xièxiènín

no, thanks 不, 谢谢 bù, xièxie

thanks very much 多谢 duōxiè

that 那 nà

that one 那一个 nàyīgè

the: *the book/girl/house/man* 书/男人/女孩/房子 shū/nánrén/nǔhái/fángzi

theatre 剧院 jùyuàn

theft 盗窃 dàoqiè

their 他们的 tāmende

them (boys, men, mixed) 他们 tāmen

(girls, women) 她们 tāmen

then 当时 dāngshí

there (over there) 那里 nàlǐ

there is/there are 有 yǒu

there isn't.../there aren't any... 没有… méi yǒu…

these 这些 zhèxiē

they 他们 tāmen

thick 厚 hòu de

thief 小偷 xiǎotōu

thigh 大腿 dàtuǐ

thin 薄的 báo de

thing 事 shì

(belongings) 东西 dōngxi

think 思考 sīkǎo

third 第三 dìsān

thirsty: *to be thirsty* 渴了 kěle

thirteen 十三 shísān

thirty 三十 sānshí

this 这个 zhègé

this man 这个男人 zhègè nánrén

thorn 刺 cì

those 那些 nàxiē

those people/books 那些人/书 nàxiē rén/shū

a thousand 一千 yīqiān

thread 线 xiàn

three 三 sān

thriller 惊险 jīngxiǎn

throat 喉咙 hóulóng

Thursday 星期四 xīngqīsì

ticket (bus, train etc) 车票 chēpiào

adult ticket 成人票 chéngrénpiào

child ticket 儿童票 értóngpiào

return ticket 往返票 wǎngfǎnpiào

single ticket 单程票 dānchéngpiào

student ticket 学生票 xuéshēngpiào

ticket office 售票处 shòupiàochù

tide (sea) 潮汐 cháoxī

tidy 整洁的 zhěngjié de

tie 领带 lǐngdài

tight 紧绷的 jǐnbēng de

tights 裤袜 kùwà

tile (floor, wall) 砖 zhuān

(roof) 瓦 wǎ

till 收银台 shōuyíntái

time 时间 shíjiān

at what time...? 什么时间…? shénme shíjiān?

what time is it? 几点了? jǐdiǎn le?

timetable 时刻表 shíkèbiǎo

tin 锡 xī

tinfoil 锡纸 xīzhǐ

tin opener 开罐器 kāiguànqì

tip (for service) 小费 xiǎofèi

to tip (waiter) 付小费 fùxiǎofèi

tired 累的 lèi de

tissue (handkerchief) 纸巾 zhǐjīn

to 到 dào

to France/London/school/the station 去法国/伦敦/学校/车站 qù Fǎguó/Lúndūn/xuéxiào/chēzhàn

toast (bread) 烤面包 kǎomiànbāo (drink) 祝酒 zhùjiǔ

tobacco 香烟 xiāngyān

tobacconist's 香烟店 xiāngyāndiàn

today 今天 jīntiān

toddler 学步的小孩 xuébù de xiǎohái

toe 脚趾 jiǎozhǐ

together 一起 yīqǐ

toilet 厕所 cèsuǒ

toilet paper 卫生纸 wèishēngzhǐ

toiletries 卫生用品 wèishēng yòngpǐn

tomato 西红柿 xīhóngshì

tomatoes (tin) 西红柿罐头 xīhóngshì guàntou

tomato sauce 西红柿酱 xīhóngshì jiàng

tomorrow 明天 míngtiān

tomorrow morning 明天早晨 míngtiān zǎochén

tongue 舌头 shétou

tonight 今晚 jīnwǎn

tonsillitis 扁桃腺炎 biǎntáoxiànyán

too 太 tài

tool 用具 yòngjù

tool kit 工具包 gōngjùbāo

tooth 牙 yá

toothache 牙疼 yáténg

toothbrush 牙刷 yáshuā

toothpaste 牙膏 yágāo

toothpick 牙签 yáqiān

top 顶部 dǐngbù

torch 手电筒 shǒudiàntǒng

to be torn 在两者中游移不定 zài liǎngzhě zhōng yóuyí bùdìng

total 总的 zǒng de

touch 触觉 chùjué

tough (meat) 老的 lǎo de

tour 旅行 lǚxíng

tourist information 游客资讯 yóukè zīxùn

tourist office 旅游咨询处 lǚyóu zīxúnchù

tow 拖 tuō

towel 毛巾 máojīn

tower 塔 tǎ

town 城镇 chéngzhèn

town centre 市中心 shì zhōngxīn

town hall 市政厅 shìzhèngtīng

tow rope 拖绳 tuōshéng

toxic 有毒的 yǒudú de

toy shop 玩具店 wánjùdiàn

toys 玩具 wánjù

tracksuit 运动服 yùndòngfú

traditional 传统的 chuántǒng de

traffic 交通 jiāotōng

traffic jam 交通阻塞 jiāotōng zǔsè

traffic lights 交通灯 jiāotōngdēng

traffic warden 交通管理员 jiāotōng guǎnlǐyuán

trailer 拖车 tuōchē

train 火车 huǒchē

trainers 运动鞋 yùndòngxié

tram 有轨电车 yǒuguǐ diànchē

tranquillizer 镇静剂 zhènjìngjì

transfer 转移 zhuǎnyí

to translate 翻译 fānyì
translation 译文 yìwén
to travel 旅行 lǚxíng
travel agent's 旅行社 lǚxíngshè
traveller's cheque 旅行支票 lǚxíng zhīpiào
travel insurance 旅行保险 lǚxíng bǎoxiǎn
travel sickness 晕车/船/机症 yùnchē/chuán/jī zhèng
tray 托盘 tuōpán
tree 树 shù
trip 出行 chūxíng
trolley 手推车 shǒutuīchē
trouble 麻烦 máfan
trousers 裤子 kùzi
trout 鳟鱼 zūnyú
truck 卡车 kǎchē
true 真实的 zhēnshí de
truth 事实 shìshí
Tuesday 星期二 xīngqī'èr
tulip 郁金香 yùjīnxiāng
tumble dryer 滚筒干衣机 gǔntǒng gānyījī
tuna 金枪鱼 jīnqiāngyú
tunnel 隧道 suìdào
turkey 火鸡 huǒjī
turn 转变 zhuǎnbiàn
to turn off/on (light etc) 关/开 guān/kāi
turnip 萝卜 luóbo
tweezers 镊子 nièzi
twelve 十二 shí'èr
twenty 二十 èrshí
twice 两次 liǎngcì
twin (beds) 成对的单人床 chéngduì de dānrénchuáng
(brother, sister) 孪生的 luánshēng de
two 二 èr
type 种类 zhǒnglèi
typical 典型的 diǎnxíng de
tyre 轮胎 lúntāi
tyre pressure 轮胎气压 lúntāi qìyā

U

ugly 丑陋的 chǒulòu de
ulcer 溃疡 kuìyáng
umbrella 雨伞 yǔsǎn
uncle (father's older brother) 伯父 bófù
(father's younger brother) 叔父 shūfù
(mother's brother) 舅父 jiùfù
uncomfortable 不舒服的 bù shūfu de
unconscious 失去知觉的 shīqù zhījué de
under 在 … 下面 zài … xiàmian
underground (metro) 地铁 dìtiě
underground station 地铁站 dìtiězhàn
underpants 内裤 nèikù
to understand 明白 míngbai
do you understand? 你明白吗? nǐ míngbai ma?
I don't understand 我不明白 wǒ bù míngbai
underwear 内衣 nèiyī
undo 解开 jiěkāi
undress 脱衣服 tuō yīfu
unemployed 失业的 shīyè de
unfasten 解开 jiěkāi
unhappy 愁苦的 chóukǔ de
United Kingdom 英国 Yīngguó
United States 美国 Měiguó
university 大学 dàxué
unleaded 无铅汽油 wúqiānqìyóu
unlikely 未必会发生的 wèibì huì fāshēng de
to unlock 开锁 kāisuǒ
unlucky 不幸的 bùxìng de
unpack 开包 kāibāo
unpleasant 使人不愉快的 shǐ rén bù yúkuài de
(manner, person) 令人讨厌的 lìng rén tǎoyàn de
unplug 拔去 … 的插头 báqù … de chātóu
unscrew 旋开 xuánkāi

until 直到 … 时 zhídào … shí
unusual 不寻常的 bù xúncháng de
up 上 shàng
upside down 上下颠倒地
  shàngxià diāndǎo de
upstairs 在楼上 zài lóushàng
urgent 紧急 jǐnjí
urine 尿 niào
us 我们 wǒmen
USA 美国 Měiguó
to use 使用 shǐyòng
useful 有用的 yǒuyòng de
usual 惯常的 guàncháng de
usually 通常地 tōngcháng de
U-turn U形转弯 U xíng zhuǎnwān

V

vacancy (in hotel) 空房 kōngfáng
vacant 空着的 kòngzhe de
vacation 度假 dùjià
vaccination 疫苗接种 yìmiáo
  jiēzhòng
vacuum cleaner 真空吸尘器
  zhēnkōng xīchénqì
vagina 阴道 yīndào
valid 有效的 yǒuxiàode
valley 山谷 shāngǔ
valuable 有价值的 yǒujiàzhíde
value 价值 jiàzhí
valve 阀 fá
van 厢式运货车 xiāngshì
  yùnhuòchē
vase 花瓶 huāpíng
VAT 增值税 zēngzhíshuì
veal 小牛肉 xiǎoniúròu
vegetables 蔬菜 shūcài
vegetarian 素食者 sùshízhě
vehicle 机动车 jīdòngchē
vein 静脉 jìngmài
Velcro® 尼龙搭扣 Nílóngdākòu
velvet 天鹅绒 tiān'éróng
vending machine 自动售货机
  zìdòng shòuhuòjī
venison 鹿肉 lùròu

very 很 hěn
vest 汗衫 hànshān
vet 兽医 shòuyī
via 经由 jīngyóu
video 录像 lùxiàng
video camera 录象机 lùxiàngjī
video cassette/tape 录像带
  lùxiàngdài
video game 电子游戏 diànzǐ
  yóuxì
video recorder 录像机 lùxiàngjī
view 景色 jǐngsè
villa 别墅 biéshù
village 乡村 xiāngcūn
vinegar 醋 cù
vineyard 葡萄园 pútáoyuán
violet 紫罗兰色的 zǐluólánsè de
virus 病毒 bìngdú
visa 签证 qiānzhèng
to visit 走访 zǒufǎng
visiting hours 探视时间 tànshì
  shíjiān
visitor 游客 yóukè
vitamin 维生素 wéishēngsù
vodka 伏特加酒 fútèjiā jiǔ
voice 声音 shēngyīn
volcano 火山 huǒshān
volleyball 排球 páiqiú
voltage 电压 diànyā
to vomit 呕吐 ǒutù
voucher 代金券 dàijīnquàn

W

wage 工资 gōngzī
waist 腰 yāo
waistcoat 马甲 mǎjiǎ
to wait (for) 等 děng
waiter/waitress 服务员
  fúwùyuán
waiting room 等候室 děnghòushì
wake up 唤醒 huànxǐng
Wales 威尔士 Wēi'ěrshì
walk 步行 bùxíng
walking stick 手杖 shǒuzhàng

Walkman® 随身听 suíshēn tīng

wall (inside) 墙 qiáng

(outside) 城墙 chéngqiáng

wallet 钱包 qiánbāo

walnut 核桃 hétao

to want 想 xiǎng

I want... 我想… wǒ xiǎng...

we want... 我们想… wǒmen xiǎng...

war 战争 zhànzhēng

ward 病房 bìngfáng

wardrobe 衣橱 yīchú

warehouse 仓库 cāngkù

warm 温暖的 wēnnuǎnde

are you warm enough?
你觉得够暖和吗? nǐ juéde gòu nuǎnhe ma?

it's warm 天很暖和 tiān hěn nuǎnhe

warning 警告 jǐnggào

to wash 洗 xǐ

washbasin 脸盆 liǎnpén

washcloth 毛巾 máojīn

washing machine 洗衣机 xǐyījī

washing powder 洗衣粉 xǐyīfěn

washing-up 待洗餐具 dàixǐ cānjù

washing-up liquid 洗洁剂 xǐjié jì

wasp sting 黄蜂叮刺 huángfēngdīngcì

wastepaper basket 废纸篓 fèizhǐlǒu

watch 手表 shǒubiǎo

watchstrap 表带 biǎodài

water 水 shuǐ

boiled water 开水 kāishuǐ

cold water 冷水 lěngshuǐ

hot water 热水 rèshuǐ

mineral water 矿泉水 kuàngquánshuǐ

non-drinking water 非饮用水 fēi yǐnyòngshuǐ

sparkling water 有汽泡的 yǒu qìpàode

still water 无汽泡的 wú qìpàode

watercress 水田芥 shuǐtiánjiè

waterfall 瀑布 pùbù

watermelon 西瓜 xīguā

waterproof 防水的 fángshuǐ de

water-skiing 去滑水 qùhuáshuǐ

water sports 水上运动 shuǐshang yùndòng

wave 挥动 huīdòng

wax 蜡 là

way 路 lù

way in 入口 rùkǒu

way out 出口 chūkǒu

we 我们 wǒmen

weak 虚弱的 xūruò de

to wear 穿 chuān

weather 天气 tiānqì

weather forecast 天气预报 tiānqì yùbào

website 网址 wǎngzhǐ

wedding 婚礼 hūnlǐ

wedding anniversary 结婚纪念日 jiéhūn jìniànrì

wedding dress 婚纱 hūnshā

wedding ring 结婚戒指 jiéhūn jièzhi

Wednesday 星期三 xīngqīsān

week 星期 xīngqīng

weekday 工作日 gōngzuòrì

weekend 周末 zhōumò

at the weekend 在周末 zài zhōumò

last/next/this weekend
上周末/下周末/这个周末 shàngzhōu mò/xiàzhōu mò/zhègè zhōumò

weekly 每周 měizhōu

weekly magazine 周刊杂志 zhōukānzázhì

weigh 称 … 的重量 chēng ... de zhòngliàng

welcome 欢迎 huānyíng

you're welcome! 不客气! bù kèqì!

well (healthy) 身体好的 shēntǐ hǎo de

wellington boot 橡胶长统靴
xiàngjiāo chángtǒngxuē
Welsh 威尔士的 Wēi'ěrshì de
(language) 威尔士语 Wēi'ěrshìyǔ
west 西方 xīfāng
wet 湿的 shī de
(weather) 多雨的 duōyǔ de
what 什么 shénme
what is it? 那是什么? nàshì
shénme?
what's your name? 你叫什么名字?
nǐ jiào shénme míngzi?
wheat 小麦 xiǎomài
wheel 车轮 chēlún
wheelchair 轮椅 lúnyǐ
wheel clamp 车轮固定夹 chēlún
gùdìngjiā
when 什么时候 shénme shíhòu
where 哪里 nǎli
where are you from? 你是哪里人?
nǐ shì nǎli rén?
where can I/we go…?
我/我们去哪儿可以…?
wǒ/wǒmen qu nǎr kěyǐ…?
where is…? 在哪儿…? zài nǎr…?
which 哪一个 nǎyīgè
while 一会儿 yīhuìr
for a while 有一会儿 yǒu yīhuìr
whipped cream 泡沫奶油 pàomò
nǎiyóu
whisky 威士忌酒 wēishìjìjiǔ
white 白色的 báisède
who 谁 shuí
whole 整个的 zhěnggè de
wholemeal 全麦的 quánmài de
whose: *whose is it?* 那是谁的?
nàshì shuíde?
why 为什么 wèishénme
wide 宽的 kuān de
widow 寡妇 guǎfù
widower 鳏夫 guānfū
width 宽度 kuāndù
wife 妻子 qīzi
wig 假发 jiǎfà

to win 赢 yíng
wind 风 fēng
windmill 风车 fēngchē
window 窗户 chuānghù
windscreen 挡风玻璃
dǎngfēngbōli
windscreen washer
挡风玻璃清洗器 dǎngfēngbōli
qīngxǐqì
windscreen wiper
挡风玻璃刮水器 dǎngfēngbōli
guāshuǐqì
windsurfing 帆板运动 fānbǎn
yùndòng
windy 有风的 yǒufēng de
wine 葡萄酒 pútáojiǔ
red wine 红葡萄酒 hóng pútáojiǔ
white wine 白葡萄酒 bái pútáojiǔ
wine glass 酒杯 jiǔbēi
wine list 酒水单 jiǔshuǐdān
wing 翅膀 chìbǎng
wing mirror 侧视镜 cèshì jìng
winter 冬天 dōngtiān
wire 金属丝 jīnshǔsī
with a double bed 有双人床 yǒu
shuāngrénchuáng
with bath 有浴缸 yǒu yùgāng
with ice 加冰 jiābīng
with lemon 加柠檬 jiā níngméng
with milk 加奶 jiānǎi
with shower 有淋浴 yǒu línyù
with sugar 加糖 jiātáng
without 不加 bùjiā
without ice 不加冰 bùjiā bīng
without milk 不加奶 bùjiā nǎi
without sugar 不加糖 bùjiā táng
witness 目击者 mùjīzhě
wok 炒菜锅 chǎocàiguō
wolf 狼 láng´
woman 女士 nǚshì
wonderful 绝妙的 juémiào de
wood 木材 mùcái
wool 羊毛 yángmáo

word 词 cí
work 工作 gōngzuò
world 世界 shìjiè
worldwide 世界范围的 shìjiè fànwéi de
worse 更坏的 gènghuài de
worth 价值 jiàzhí
wrap 披肩 pījiān
wrapping paper 牛皮纸 niúpízhǐ
wrinkle 皱纹 zhòuwén
wrist 手腕 shǒuwàn
write 写 xiě
please write it down 请把它写下来 qǐng bǎ tā xiěxiàlái
writing paper 信纸 xìnzhǐ
wrong 不恰当的 bù qiàdàng de

X

x ray X光 X guāng
to x ray 照X光 zhào X guāng

Y

yacht 游艇 yóu tǐng
year 年 nián
last year 去年 qùnián
next year 明年 míngnián

this year 今年 jīnnián
yellow 黄色的 huángsède
yes 是 shì
yes, please 好，谢谢 hǎo, xièxie
yesterday 昨天 zuótiān
yet: *not yet* 还没有 háiméiyǒu
yoghurt 酸奶 suānnǎi
pot of yoghurt 一盒酸奶 yī hé suānnǎi
yolk 蛋黄 dànhuáng
you 你/你们 nǐ/nǐmen
and you? 你呢? nǐ ne?
young 年轻的 niánqīngde
(people) 年轻人 niánqīngrén
your 你的/你们的 nǐde/nǐmende
youth hostel 青年招待所 qīngnián zhāodàisuǒ

Z

zebra crossing 斑马线 bānmǎxiàn
zero 零 líng
zip 拉链 lāliàn
zone 区域 qūyù
zoo 动物园 dòngwùyuán
to zoom past/along 疾驰而过/沿 … 疾驰 jíchí ér guò/yán … jíchí

Further titles in Collins' phrasebook range
Collins Gem Phrasebook

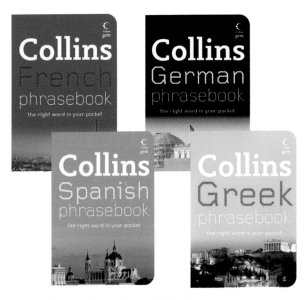

Also available as **Phrasebook CD Pack**

Other titles in the series

Afrikaans
Arabic
Cantonese
Croatian
Czech
Dutch
Italian

Japanese
Korean
Latin American
 Spanish
Mandarin
Polish
Portuguese

Russian
Thai
Turkish
Vietnamese
Xhosa
Zulu

Collins Phrasebook and Dictionary

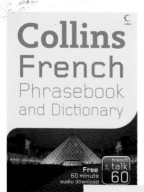

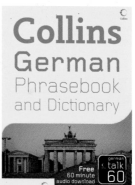

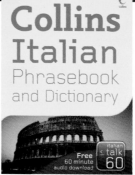

Other titles in the series
Greek Japanese Mandarin Polish Portuguese Spanish Turkish

Collins Easy: Photo Phrasebook

Also available as
**Phrasebook
CD Pack**

**Other titles
in the series**
Easy French
Easy Greek
Easy Italian

To order any of these titles, please telephone 0870 787 1732.
For further information about all Collins books, visit our website:
www.collins.co.uk